Corn Stories:

The Detasseler's Bible

Fanciful Accountings of 99.7% True Events

by

JJ McNiece

For Corn Warriors
past, present & future

Corn is cleaned with wind,
and the Soul with chastening.

– George Herbert

Contents

Argumentum

Dear Reader,

Once, I was an Arkansas college student (Hendrix College '02) who drove up to Iowa in the summertimes for corn detasseling. The job only lasted through July, and it paid well. Still, those incentives motivated me less than a strong desire to drink beer and smoke weed with my friends.

After college, I graduated from law school, hung an attorney's shingle, and steadily forgot about corn detasseling. In seven long years of legal practice, I learned one valuable lesson: lawyering's a vile profession of Pig Latin ventriloquists. And yet, rather than pry off my shingle, responsibly, I waited around and suffered a mental health breakdown instead. That's when lawyering flip-flopped inside of me from a reflex into a role I couldn't even playact.

Which led to Poetry. During my breakdown, I met Poetry like how a drowner greets a lifeguard: wailing, flailing, and in need of a punch to the nose before I dragged us both down. (In my defense, this is how most people meet Poetry.) Intrepidly, Poetry saved me despite myself. In due course, I amassed professionals, prescriptions, self-knowledge & psychological edification. Still, Poetry remained the root and wellspring of my convalescence.

But here's the thing: that was ten years ago. I'm better now. And I can write about something other than the lint in my navel.

But what, Dear Reader, to choose?

Well...

Ever since college, whenever I have breached the topic of corn detasseling, it has roused people's curiosity. Immensely. If I had $9.95 for every time someone asked me *What the hell is corn detasseling?* my mental health would be flourishing. Accordingly, I aim to give my audience the one book they've been clamoring for.

And yeah, I get it—This all sounds ridiculous. Ten years of therapy, Zoloft & self-focused poems, has led me to the conclusion that people want to read about Corn. Tailor my straitjacket. But I'm telling you, people damn near accost me: *What the hell is corn detasseling? What the hell is corn detasseling?* the moment I mention it.

In fact, I'd wager that question is now forefront in *your* mind, Dearest Reader. Do you recall any interest in my education, legal career, mental health or homeopathic poetry?

I sure as hell hope not!

So... What the hell is corn detasseling? Well, it's complicated. I wrote this book to answer that question, comprehensively. In the main, this compendium, naturally, assembles some of my very best stories from Corn. I detasseled for six summers, so I've got bushels of yarns. But, I've also shuffled all of my detasseling know-how into the plots, so that this book'll serve you double as a manual/guide for corn detasseling too. In other words, it'll teach you how to make money in the cornfields.

Hell, there's a good chance I'll see you out there!

Your faithful scribbler,
Double Trouble

Preface

Wisconsin apple pickers. Texas toilet-paper-tree planters. California berry pickers. They'll all tell you the same thing: "Corn detasselers are fucking insane. Just listen to this..." Then they'll rattle off an anecdote you'll likely disbelieve. For within the seasonal migrant farming community, corn detasselers are Legends. Rock Stars. Years before I detasseled corn, detasseler-celebrity had long enthralled this nation's wide circuit of hard-farming hippies. And I rocked the Corn twenty years ago. Detasselers remain notorious today.

But is the reputation justified? Are corn detasselers, truly, a breed apart? Maybe detasseling corn, itself, smelts these Heavy Machetes—the labor, the crucible? Maybe annual hordes of Arkansans infused some of the Natural State into the avocation? Could be the Texans' big and bright stamp of their own is to blame? Or, maybe corn detasselers are just fucking insane?

All that and more awaits your exploration and judgment, Dear Reader. I but exhibit such evidence as I can swear to. The truth. The whole truth. And nothing but. However, I do stipulate to altering people's names. To protect such parties from ruin of course. Other than my own name and a handful of others (which I'll explain later), I employ aliases and sobriquets. But the rest of this shit is on the level. Aside from conflating some events, mere compression for your reading pleasure, and disguising a few locations, all this stuff really happened folks! (Pretty much.)

So, grab you a cold beer. Smoke a bowl. Sit back and listen to testimony. Or what migrant farmers would know better by the name of "Corn Stories."

Horsepower

Or *The Shotgun Siren of Hucksters, Hustlers & Outlaws*

"I am the Corn Destroyer," I howl. "I am the Tassel Terminator!"

I am twenty years old. Stoned. In the middle of Iowa. Pulling tassels from genetically modified seed corn. Well, I was. That hollering's got me thirsty, so now I'm just standing here sucking water through the bite-valve hose on my Camelbak (mini backpack that sheaths a 3-liter bladder).

It's July. 2001. Evening. 80 °F? A light, steady breeze fans me. The sun will set in an hour. I know this because Heath Phillips, a Wisconsin detasseler (who you'll meet in a later story), taught me a trade secret my rookie year: With an open palm, arm extended, put your pinky flush to the horizon line & tuck your thumb down; now just stack your hands, pinkies-against-pointers like that, until one hand is touching the sun. Each hand length (sans thumb) between the horizon line and the sun is equal to one hour before sunset. Works great out here in Iowa. Where their "rolling hills" are flat.

But I digress.

I spin around & admire the view.

To my left, past a buffer zone of male corn plants, lies a well-paved county road—its shoulders lined with the mangy, hangdog jalopies of migrant corn detasselers. Across the street, a rolling irrigation machine, one-quarter of a mile in length, drives itself around a 500-acre soybean field. That's right: a self-propelled sprinkler, big as a cruise ship, makes scattered summer showers—Iowa-style.

Whereas to my right, a glinting green sea of corn sprawls across the panorama. Five-feet tall. Gently waving dollar signs. Regal and pacific. Except for Roman (a.k.a. "Ramen" like the noodles) Holiday, my hometown friend and former college

14

roommate, scudding up on me like a warship. Better quit fucking around. Shouldn't have stopped to finish that bowl.

The tassels fly.

There's a music to detasseling corn: *Pop. Pop. Ssss . . . Pop. Ssss . . . Pop. Pop. Pop. Ssss . . . Pop. Pop. Pop. Ssss . . . Pop.* That *Ssss* sound is the damp, suctiony protest the tassels—which look like bulbous, feathered quills by the way—will murmur sometimes coming loose. And those *Pops* sound like pulling out wine corks. The corn in this field's been lilting fairly sweetly for me. So I'd classify it "Butter" corn. Conversely, ornery corn'll BOOM: *Ssss . . . PunNCKT! Ssss . . . PunNCKT! Ssss . . . PUNCKT!* Like a hissing cobra banging its head against a kettle drum. You hear that clangor, you know you're pulling "Bullshit" corn.

There's a rhythm to detasseling too. Hand over fist, hand over fist, hand over fist. Churning. Like a riverboat paddlewheel spitting out noodly, lime-green tassels instead of fish.

Lastly, there's a pace to detasseling. That's your gait. Your stride. We'd all run out here if we could. But all that jostling makes you miss too many tassels. Prior to our arrival, machines mow then pull a field anywhere from 50 to 95 % clean. (Hopefully.) But they need it 99.7%. So, you zip-zoom-scoot as fast as you can without sabotaging your tassel vision: and that's your pace.

Myself, I enjoy a long stride. Stiltish. Got big arms and shoulders too. But on account of my waist's armpit fetish, my rhythm's always tripping over my pace. Makes me a bit of a wrecking ball. Holiday on the other hand, he's nimble. His stride's long too, but not inhumanly-so like my own. I've got him beat on pace. But he bests me when it comes to rhythm. That's because Holiday generates his arm speed and power through his core. "More endurance that way," he says.

And he's right—Holiday's rice hat is now much nearer than before.

"I am the Maize Mutilator," I self-motivate. "The Dragon

Detasseler."

This is the third consecutive summer Holiday & I have worked Corn. Our first season, we earned more money than any other rookies on our crew. Our second season—last summer—we earned the most money flat out. This year? We've been traveling all over Iowa, at the behest of the big shots, to detassel during the peaks of five different crews' seasons. Very much like calling in the calvary. For Holiday & I are "Horses," in detasseling lingo.

Detasselers earn piecework wages. Even massive cornfields like this one (500 acres; it's the rotational sibling of that soybean field across the street) have a limited number of "Blocks." Blocks, a.k.a. "Panels," are four neat rows of female plants sown between single rows of males. (See Visual Aids.) The faster you detassel the four female rows, the faster you can sign your name onto your next block. Thusly, one or two extra panels, every field, every day, adds up profitably. (As does working five crews in one summer.)

Prior to blue Sharpeeing our names onto this field's final two blank tags, Holiday and I hadn't seen much of one another this afternoon. Still, we were the only two crew members to procure a seventh panel. And we knew it. (We read every tag.) So, about 200 feet into these blocks, we plopped down & smoked a celebratory bowl of dank ass nuggets.

After that, of course, we raced.

I quickly gained a hare's to tortoise lead. Smiling, cruising through my first row of butter corn, I felt no sympathy as Holiday caterwauled and trudged through patch upon patch of bullshit corn. Usually, it's the bookend blocks where you get screwed—at the field's edges. And I got the very last block. Hence, Holiday's frustration.

But I fear I may have spoiled my early lead.

Smack! The hard button of a tassel beans me square in the back.

"HOLY SHIT!" I cry. "Muther Fucker!"

I'm on Holiday's left, so he has the advantage ballistically. I can fling a tassel 50 feet into a coffee cup—with my right arm. But so can Holiday. I loose a couple southpaw volleys, but it's no use. Better to stay focused on the tassels, with my eye on that upcoming—& final—turn. I make a helmet of my straw hat and pick up the pace.

Pop. Pop. Pop. Ssss . . . Pop. Pop. Pop. I'm conducting a goddam corncerto over here.

And yet . . .

That telltale whoosh of redlining horsepower crescendos behind me.

Corn leaves grow thick as vinyl. They slap the shit out of you too. And the stalks rake up against your hips, underarms & chest. Consequently, a charging detasseler can clippety-clop up one hell of a clatter. Right now, the din of Holiday's detasseling back there just kind of buzzes. Like cicadas. Or an A/C condenser. Kind of ambient. That means he's 50 feet out, nearabout. If he gets to 20 feet, that buzz'll favor a swarm of hornets. At 10 feet? A tornado.

Being as how this is a first pull & these are half-mile rows, more jockeying WILL transpire. First pulls are a dash (zip-zoom-scoot), one row at a time. We'll return for a second pull two days from now. So, if I miss a few tassels... they'll keep. And if you're wondering, there's no avoiding second pulls. Nobody can pass inspection after just one pull and make good money doing it. On the other side of that continuum, you don't want your crew boss wondering after a first pull if you were detasseling or just signing your name onto tags. Plus, second pulls are supposed to be a stroll—eyeballing and detasseling two rows at a time. A lot of hairy second pulls & the rest of your crew will beat you, badly, getting over to the next field. They'll be signing more blank tags, making more money, while you're stuck shoring up cash you already banked.

Swish-swoosh-shwip-shwoo-ship! rents five-tassels over my head. A bundled payload: their feathery ends twisted and intertwined. These dive-bombers tend to stay together till their apogee, then spread out on the comedown. Kind of like tassel buckshot. More's the fool I am for not thinking of it first—I'm in no mood to lose this race.

Pop. Pop. Ssss . . . Pop. Ssss . . . Pop. Pop. Pop. Ssss . . . Pop. Pop. Pop, my corn croons.

Tornado . . . Hornet's nest . . . crickets, Holiday's corn counter-harmonizes.

So I'm about 300 feet from the final turn now. In horseracing parlance, this is called the "Stretch." I've restored my lead, appreciably. I missed a few tassels I otherwise would have terminated, but the quality of my work still cuts the mustard—for a first pull. But make no mistake, this horserace is far from over. Holiday *will* make another charge. Possibly two or three.

Steeled, I keep an eye to the corn, an eye to the sky &

the tassels fly.

Welp, I'm 100 feet from the turn now. And boy am I FUCKED. The machines missed every goddam plant from here to the end. Next row over, too. Holiday's gaining on me. I don't know which'll be worse: him passing me up, or laughing maniacally as he does so. I've got one gambit to escape doom. And it's dicey. There is a frowned upon practice in corn detasseling, called "Treeing," whereby rather than popping out the tassel one instead grabs the plant stalk just below the tassel and rips it down & out like an arm wrestler. Please Reader, DO NOT TREE THE CORN! It dishonors you. But as for me: I've got

18

a race to win. And these half-mile rows provide great cover for it, usually. Thing is, this is the end of my block. Where some farmer or seed company bigwig's likely to chance upon any wanton paths of destruction. Hence, dicey. Nevertheless, these *are* practiced hands. And I *am* the Dragon Detasseler. Plus, I'm sly enough to detassel the last 20 to 25 feet on the level.

Fuck it. Let's roll the dice:

"FUCK THIS GOD DAMN FUCKING BULL-SHIT! MUTHER FUCKER! FUCK YOU! FUCK THIS! FUUUUUUUUUCK!"

Having completed Row Three, I make the final turn. And there's Holiday! 30 feet out and hauling ass. For he knows that the turn provides him with an enhanced opportunity to cut into my lead. And that's true regardless of whether or not my block's infested with tassels. Sprinting into and out of a turn will gain Holiday more ground than would the same effort expended on a straightaway. In horseracing, this is called "Riding the Rail." And it works the same in a cornfield.

"Slow down Asshole," I shout. "You're missing too many tassels."

"Fuck you dude. Coming through," Holiday snorts.

No run-of-the-mill detasseler is Ramen Holiday. Nevertheless, he'll serve us well to model the job's quotidian apparel. Holiday sports a light, long-sleeve, button-down cotton shirt. It is filthy. To prevent cuts, he has tied a red bandana to his neck. As mentioned, a waxy, conical rice hat shades his face. Blackout sunglasses (seed company-issued) protect his eyes. Headphones arc round his head. Audio wires droop into the side pocket of his Camelbak. Wherein his MiniDisc player nests inside of a Ziploc bag. While most detasselers wear light cotton pants or shorts, a small number (like me) wear cutoff jeans. But not Holiday. He wears a skirt. Specifically, a calico, ankle-length boho— or "hippie skirt." Shoes? Well, they were once tennis shoes. But

19

of what make and model, none shall ever know again. And, lest we forget the Duct Tape. As horses DO NOT wear gloves, Holiday's fingers are silver & tanned candy canes, leaving his lucrative fingertips dexterously free & tactile. Lastly, and perhaps most importantly, Holiday sports the gap-toothed, crooked grin of a hustler.

"Missed a few that I can see," I chastise. "You're gonna get called back on this one dude." It's mental warfare. I'm taking a breather at the end of my rows, hoping to throw Holiday off his rhythm.

"Fuck off Jackass! This is a first pull." He pauses at the turn. (Success!)

"You don't say. I was so stoned I must have forgot."

"Any of that bowl left?"

"Nothing you'd want to hit."

"Dickhead."

"Yeah."

"Nice fucking work back there," he scoffs. "Looks like a goddam elephant somersaulted through your block."

"Haha. Yeah, I'll keep an eye out."

"Well... Peace."

The tassels fly.

Twenty. five. feet. of. detasseling. every. single. fucking. plant. SUCKS! But you gotta do it at the fronts and backs of your blocks. And really, it's 100 feet. Not 25, like what I just did. But Holiday's got the lead now! So... Please look away Reader, while I tree to catch up.

"MUTHER FUCKER! FUCK YOU! FUUUUUUK..."
Etc.

Whew! Well, I ain't proud of myself—got pretty bullish & pink back there. Notwithstanding, I've worked my way out of

20

that patch of bullshit. More importantly, I'm still in this race: Holiday's only got me by 100 feet or so.

Are you thinking what I'm thinking?

A quick sprint and I'm in range.

Swish-swoosh-shwip-shwoo-ship—

—Smack! Sm-sm-smack! Smack!

"GOD DAMN IT," Holiday protests. "Stop it Muther Fucker!" He pivots. Then flings a tassel cross the Rubicon.

And our race descends into combat. We're still detasseling, mind you—because we're horses. But our paces ebb. While our rhythms transition smoothly over to the war economy. As well as our mindsets. Indeed, we may well pause this race. Smoke some more peacekeeping nuggets? It *has* been a long day. These *are* our seventh panels.

But our whole crew is watching us! And we notice it at the same time. Holiday's super competitive. Like quit–shit–if–he's–not–good–at–it competitive. Me? People say I'm trying to outman my Pops out here. So we both want to be the best. Bad.

And now everybody's watching!

Thus, arrows are quivered, treaties are signed &

the tassels fly.

Pop. Pop. Pop. Ssss . . . Pop, singsongs my corn.

Pop. Pop. Pop. Ssss . . . Pop, warbles Holiday's.

"You're gonna get called back for sure dude," I say. (More mental warfare.)

"You already said that dipshit."

(Yes. I did.)

"Haven't been called back in three years," he continues. (Success! I'm in his head.)

"Yeah. Me neither. But you usually can't keep up with me. So—"

—Smack! (A timely hit.)

We're stride for stride, 1200 . . . 1190 . . . 1180 feet from the finish line.

Now I can't tell you, exactly, why Merle Beaver would sabotage a fair & square detasseling horserace. But I can speculate. And indeed, I enjoy such conjecture—it helps pass the time out here. First off, Merle Beaver is a Texan. Deep. In the heart. A chestnut colt running with a herd of Austinites, Beaver and company stack up shoe-to-shoe with us Arkansas thoroughbreds. Could've easily been two of them snagging seven panels today instead of us. So, maybe rivalry explains some of why Beaver's marching with a glare and a scowl into Holiday's block.

Secondly, and I don't mean to sound prejudice, but maybe Beaver's making a roadblock of himself in Holiday's corn because they're both skirt-wearers. I know. I know. But hear me out on this. One would think whether a detasseler wears a skirt or not would be decided, 100%, according to chaffing. Bad chaffing equals skirt. None to light chaffing equals pants or shorts. (Such was my own analysis.) But practical concerns have proven as irrelevant as gender in predicting skirt preferences among detasselers. So, why do these skirt-wearers possess such strikingly similar personalities? I don't know. Why does their cornmanship so often reek of sorcery? Again, I know not. But this I do know, and you can take it for Gospel: skirt-wearing detasselers wield a mendacity so diabolical, pick one at random & they'll dupe the Devil into a snipe hunt. Me? I'm good at this job. Elite. I've got mental warfare and a knockout right hook. But skirt-wearers are fucking Lokis.

For instance, it would NEVER occur to me to squat in somebody's else's block of corn and take a shit. And yet, it's clear now that that's what Beaver's doing. Clenching two corn stalks on opposite rows as if they were handrails in a handicapped bathroom stall, he aims his bare ass down upon the very spot where Holiday and I smoked our rub–it–in–everybody's–face (celebratory) bowl.

And instantly, I don't give a damn about racing. You know?

22

This Beaver development's just too goddam hilarious.

Holiday's motivations about-face too of course. His just land different. "WHAT THE FUCK ARE YOU DOING MERLE," he yells. Then, Holiday starts running TOWARDS Beaver. Why? God only knows. Holiday's fucking pissed. But he's still pulling tassels the whole way—as horses do.

I keep pace so I won't miss anything.

"Gotta take a shit man," Beaver explains. "Sorry. Can't wait."

"GET THE FUCK OUT OF MY CORN!"

"This is the only bit of this good ass-wiping plant around here man. Awww . . . <!#!#!>," Beaver shits.

"FUUUUUUUCK!" Holiday's anger surrenders to shock.

Now, don't you presume for one second disgusted Reader that skirt wearing is about easy-access pooping. Foremost, none of these bastards go commando—that's fucking SUICIDE. Second, we all poop in the cornfields. In that respect, Beaver does have a point: nobody wants to wipe their ass with corn leaves. Well, nobody except for maybe Beaver. In any event, there's a weed that grows in and around the cornfields called velvetleaf. Velvetleaf is the Charmin of the fieldhand. If you spot a clump of these fat, Angel Soft, crocodile-green leaves, go ahead and Cottonelle 'em. You'll be tickled Naturelle you did. This Ultra-Plush insider scoop may even sucker you into believing the acting job being put on by Beaver here—who could've pooped anywhere. Such convincing liars, these skirt-wearers. In truth, prevaricate provocateurs & duplicitous schemers, all.

Here's how I see it: Beaver believes Holiday and I cheated. For he can explain his six panels to our seven in no other way. So, after sitting on the sidelines stewing, Beaver has to go & poop in Holiday's corn. Just to calm down. Again, Beaver's a skirt-wearer. Skirt-wearers would never just come out and say, "Yeah. So, I think you purposefully and fraudulently pulled poorly today so that you could unfairly obtain an extra block. Which I should have earned because (unlike you) I pull both rapidly and pristinely. Therefore, to exact retribution and to regain my own emotional balance, I'm going to shit in your corn Holiday." Nor would Holiday understand a word of any of that. Instead of course, Beaver said, "This is the only bit of this good ass-wiping plant around here man. Awww ..."

But I'm not buying it. And I don't think you should either Reader. Holiday sure as hell knows better. Still, why don't we just let the Lokis play their perfidious games... while I slide on by?

Pop. Pop. Pop. Ssss ... Pop.

Well, oh my. It seems I'm strolling, quite uncontested, to the end.

Pop. Pop. Pop. Ssss ... Pop.

The victor? Me?

Pop. Pop. Pop. Ssss ... Pop.

"Why yes! You did hear correctly: I *am* the Dragon Detasseler," I practice my speech. "Thank you, thank you. The Tassel Terminator? Well... if you say so."

Pop. Pop. Pop. Ssss ... Pop.

As I cross the finish line, none of the crew even notices. Whole lot of em's glued to the Holiday & Beaver shitshow. Muther Fuckers.

Oh well. A win is a win is a windfall.

So there's a snippet more to that hand-stacking-chronometer trick I described earlier: When there's only *two fingers* of daylight left, that's the sun's way of telling you to grab your booze.

I shortcut through the buffer zone, up to the road and my Jeep. Where I pop the tailgate and grab a cold six-pack of PBRs out of my beer cooler.

Then I repair to the Corntanglement.

Holiday & Beaver are detasseling leapfrog-style near the end. Beaver's still professing his innocence. Meanwhile Holiday's arguing, essentially, the same theory of the case as I gave you. Also, funnily enough, Holiday's crowing about never failing an inspection.

They cross the finish line smoking cigarettes.

While they relish their undeserved applause, I hand Holiday & Beaver a beer can each. The three of us then flick open our pocketknives, stab the can bottoms & pull the tabs—

to shotgun

start

our

new

race

to

inebriation.

Eyes watering, we stomp the cans into hockey pucks and pocket the refuse.

Then we all divine the same idea.

We're jogging now. Drinking those other PBRs (the regular way) & scurrying down Holiday's block. Sunlight fading fast.

Drawing near the final turn, I veer us over into my block. "Check this out," I say—revealing my handiwork.

Holiday laughs his ass off. "Goddam, JJ! You're fucking crazy! Bwahahahaha!"

But Beaver? Beaver looks appalled. Aghast. A bit afeared even. "Jesus Christ," he mumbles. But who knows with a guy like Beaver, right? Dude just took a shit in a cornfield.

"Yeah yeah," I say. "C'mon, we've got like... maybe five minutes."

The Iowa sun retreats, retiring unto its husk, while Holiday, Beaver & I skitter across a tractor-rutted warzone of dinosaur-scat-shaped dirt clods. For there's a field on the other side of this break we'd like to reconnoiter. As it's likely the corn we'll be pulling, come sunrise, tomorrow.

Visual Aids

500 Acre Field

1 mile by ≈ 3/4 mile (4,053 feet)
(Split into Two Detasseling Fields)

Buffer Corn—All Male Plants
60 feet

3
9
3
3

3933/18 = 218.50 Total Blocks

218.50/40 person crew =

5.46 Block Average

218.50 Total Blocks
on this side, too

Feet of Buffer Blocks

Field Break

1/2 mile blocks

Blocks = 18 feet width (3 feet between rows)

60 feet   Buffer Corn—All Male Plants Buffer Corn—All Male Plants Buffer Corn—All Male Plants

One Mile = 5,280 feet

1/2 Mile Block (a.k.a. Panel)

= 2,640 feet per row

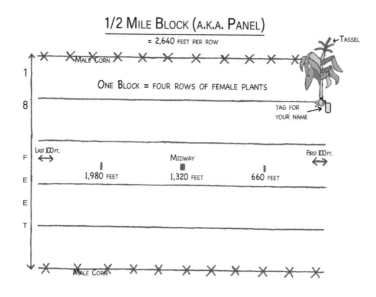

Tassel

Male Corn

1
8

One Block = four rows of female plants

Tag for
your name

Feet

Last 100 ft.   Midway   First 100 ft.

1,980 feet   1,320 feet   660 feet

Male Corn

26

Drunken Wiffle Ball
End of Season Party (1999)
– Official Rules –

1. To begin the game, the Home Team players must line up for keg stands prior to assuming their defensive positions. The Visiting Team's commencement keg stands occur prior to the bottom of the First Inning.

2. **Offense.** Upon singles, doubles & triples, baserunners receive a full cup of beer, which must be imbibed, completely, prior to crossing home plate. If not, then the runner is out & no run is scored. Upon homeruns, the slugger earns a keg stand (performed subsequent to the trot), while the other baserunners (if any) need NOT finish their beers for their runs to count in these instances. Also, there are no walks.

3. **Defense.** Errors and double plays earn one and two keg stands, respectively, from the offending fielder(s).

4. Any player may pause the game, at any time, if in pursuance of a keg stand. (There are two schools of thought on whether or not a player may pause to assist an *opponent's* keg stand. These debates can become contentious, often spilling out into the games.)

5. The winning team *must* do keg stands, sporadically, until they are losing.

6. The losing team *may* do keg stands, sporadically, until they are winning.

7. Placement of kegs is discretionary. But the dankest beer, traditionally, presides atop the pitcher's mound.

8. Fans, spectators & onlookers may abstain from drinking, but such behavior is discouraged. To that end, if you catch a foul ball you're drafted.

9. Rather than after nine innings, play stops when it's the consensus opinion of both teams that the game is over.

Interlude

When I was a teenager, thwarting the police was still a respectable way to spend a weekend. Come Monday at school, or maybe soon as Sunday at church youth group, you'd swap details of near arrests and sidestepped tickets with your buddies. Kind of like Fish Stories for Bible Belt Grunge kids. Predictably, being youngsters, me and a relevant group of my friends got a bit carried away. To us, slipping cuffs felt like a sport. Who's the smoothest criminal? Who can get nearest to those blue flames... and not get burned? Indeed, a church chaperone once dubbed us "The Disciples of Sin."

Still, we Disciples were but one iteration of a larger population: known statewide as the "Conway Hooligan." Raised on Alternative, Punk Rock & Rap; 40s, blunts & cigarettes; hiking, soccer & skateboards; the Conway Hooligan was then, as it remains today, a fiery, fearless rogue who will melt your heart. Or devour it, depending upon its mood.

All this misspent youth, its sociological insights and taxonomy, I confess to you not for absolution, judicious Reader. But rather to provide rich background and juicy depth. To facilitate your own keen enjoyment of the upcoming Corn Story. For I must admit, I did not witness the following events. Unreliable narrator, right? Sharply, critically read. But don't you worry. I heard the preceding account trumpeted, by both protagonists, so frequently during my Corn days, that I'm confident my absence will prove immaterial.

Additionally, this is the best story I've got for teaching you how to prepare for a month in Corn.

So, once again, shall we travel back in time (to one year before "Horsepower")...

Goal!

Or *The Frontier Justice of Officer Solomon*

It's the year 2000! The world has not ended, as scheduled. The computers whir and the modems crackle, as we all information superhighway ourselves into a new century—unencumbered by the shortsighted temporal coding goofs of Steve Jobs & Bill Gates. Quite surprisingly, we all find ourselves still in need of money.

So, why not detassel corn again right? Plenty of the green stuff in Iowa.

Pursuantly, me and my hometown friend and college roommate, Roman (a.k.a. "Ramen" like the noodles) Holiday, make the call to our rookie crew boss Tom Pater—a chain-smoking, avuncular spark plug from Newton County (Arkansas). And he invites us back to Scranton (Iowa). Furthermore, Tom's business partners Bob & Mona Sturgis recruit us both for their early rogueing crew in Missouri Valley. (More on rogueing in a later chapter.) Beaming with pride, I accept the extended gig immediately. Whereas Holiday figures, "Why fuck with a good thing?"

Thus, I drive up to Missouri ("MO") Valley at the end of June. And Holiday catches a ride to Scranton first of July, with a buddy of ours from Hendrix College—

Part 1 - Huckleberry Cobbs

Now, Cobbs grew up in Central Arkansas. But he did so in Clinton, rather than Conway. Geographically, Clinton's just thirty miles north of Conway. But population-wise, here in the year 2000, Clinton's south of us by 2,500 percent: 50,000 people vs. 2,500. To make matters worse, Cobbs is the six foot four inch son of their town's only cattle inspector. So who'd mess with him? Consequently, Cobbs experienced a far different adolescence than did we Conway Hooligans. And these past three years at Hendrix College, which is in Conway, has failed to mend his rural druthers.

Fortunately, Huckleberry Cobbs's callow roots will serve *you* rather well, Dearest Reader. As an avatar. For Cobbs embodies the odyssey upon which you are presently engaged: that of a wide-eyed, rookie detasseler alighting into an alien world—spoken of cryptically... stylishly mononymously... quasi-religiously as "Corn."

Anyways...

Behind Cobbs's silver sedan, the Iowa sun melts like sherbet over warm cobbler.

"Turn here," Holiday instructs.

Cobbs veers off the well-paved, two-lane highway and onto a narrow dirt road... that winds up an honest-to-God Iowa hill! The first one they've seen!

Up and up and up they climb. Holiday, pointing out potholes. Cobbs, eagle-eyed and cautious.

Three switchbacks... swiveled.

Two craters... skirted.

Then they arrive at a straightaway: twenty yards long, nearabout. Strangely, two felled corn plants lay in the center of the road fashioned into an "X." Cobbs brakes before they crunch over the stalks. Up ahead, two more corn plants are post-holed into the ground, like flags, on either side of the road. There, the lane just kind of vanishes into the sky: A blind horizon. The whole setup reminds Cobbs of X-Games events he's watched on ESPN2 The Deuce. Although these corn pylons & pennants do suggest a much tamer undertaking than all that.

"So this is it?" he asks.

"Yep. No more potholes either," Holiday confirms.

And Cobbs just fucking gooses it! Petal to the metal. Fucking VROOM!

"Goddam! You're not fucking around, are you?" Holiday smiles.

"Hehe. You swear this isn't a cliff, right?"

"Hell of a time to be asking that." Holiday braces.

WOOOO000000000—

(Let's pause here Reader for a quick breakdown—figuratively speaking—of Cobbs's silver 1997 Nissan Maxima with dookie-brown trim. Again, this is the year 2000. Maximas are cool ass cars right now. And Cobbs drives the fancy kind at that. Like SE or LE or something? But apropos of corn detasseling, this Maxima pumps iron & shits steel. Cobbs herds fucking cattle with it! Generally, trucks, SUVs & vans fare best in Corn. In that order. Nevertheless, many a car will successfully negotiate the rigors of a Corn season with vigor & aplomb.)

—000000000OOSH!

Cobbs's & Holiday's backsides drop out from under their butts. Their stomachs launch up, up, and away. Adrenaline hits 'em like Holiday's pre-roadtrip whippits. While Cobbs's Maxima, briefly, silver-streaks the stratosphere.

THUD! The Maxima's front end bonks terra firma. Cobbs & Holiday headbutt the steering wheel & the glovebox, respectively, despite wearing their seatbelts. Not hard enough to trigger the airbags, but plenty smart for bruised foreheads. Still, so far so good Maxima-wise: no rattles or pops and nothing's smoking.

Next slow-motion moment, the car's back end WHOOMPHS a landing. But it hits flush on the frame. So, no worries there? They level out, motoring along just fine. There'll be grass stains & a crack or two in the front bumper, possibly. But Cobbs is pretty sure he nailed it.

Holiday looks over approvingly.

"Bwahahahahahaha..." They bust their sides laughing.

"Man, I thought you were full of shit." Cobbs says finally.

"Told you." Holiday wipes his eyes. "Gotta ramp into Scranton Camp."

Our two principals then coast down the hill and into the campsite proper, slowly. Cobbs is riding his brakes. But not to assess the Maxima's health. Rather, because they've leapt into a bucolic fantasyland. And he's gone starry-eyed.

Acres upon acres of beautifully coiffed, manicured soybeans run up to his driver's side window like a body of water. Millions of synchronized swimming, shimmering plants wave "Hello Huckleberry. Welcome."

"Fuck Missouri Valley," Holiday proclaims—for the hundredth time. "Welcome to Detasseler Shangra-la."

And Cobbs can just feel it. Sense it. Absorb it: Scranton Camp's Elysium-ness. Nestled into the leeward slope of this veritable Iowa mountainside, soothed by the lap-lap-lapping here at Lake Soybean Superior, Scranton Camp looks like it's a three-acre lea of paradise.

And what a centerpiece! A Noah's Ark of a gray barn lords over the campsite. Big as a Clinton sale barn. Open like one too. Cobbs makes a beeline for its wide-open, north-facing door. Figuring he'll just park inside, like it's a garage.

"You'll want to stay on the road," Holiday redirects. "Swing around and park on the concrete. Under that awning."

So Cobbs wheels back around and follows the path to a slab of concrete that's as long as the Ark-barn & twice as wide. Almost like a quay. Then he drives onto it and parks under the awning—a slanted metal roof that does, technically, function as a carport.

Finally, he cuts off the engine.

"Welcome to Corn," Holiday rhapsodizes.

And Cobbs absorbs the vibe. Quite clearly, he has immigrated. The Real World, that old chestnut, has just become a foreign country: geopolitically shirked. Cobbs is now "In Corn." A Sovereign Nation unto itself. One that embraces newcomers into its bosom instantly—with a welcome wagon that squeezes Society's bullshit out of you like a rolling pin.

Holiday jumps out of the car and lights a cigarette.

Cobbs exits next. Eager to explore.

There are no walls here on the east side of the barn. "Quay-side." Just a row of Douglas fir posts. But they're thick as telephone poles & getting the job done.

Cobbs ambles inside. First thing he notices is how clean the barn is. Even the dirt floor has a shine to it. He kicks up some dust, just to make sure it smudges his boot.

A brief perambulation reveals this "barn" to be more of a hangar. Smack dab in the middle of its open floor plan sits a harvester, a tractor & some kind of robotic octopus (a detasseling machine) like hotrods on a showroom floor. All of them sparkling. John Deere green. And huge! The tractor's taller than the barndoors.

Behind Paul Bunyan's fleet, Cobbs discovers three vacant tents pitched against the barn's west wall. This being the only side of the building fully slatted & boarded up, camping here looks like smart bivouacking. It also appears, as evidenced by Holiday approaching with his weed pipe, that this sheltered locale might serve well for smoking some nuggets!

"Here." Holiday hands Cobbs the green (first) hit.

"Thanks!" Cobbs takes a toke and sits down in someone's camping chair. "So where is everybody?" He coughs.

"Walmart in Carroll. Grocery store in Jefferson. Casey's (gas station) or Tom's rental house in town. One of those three most likely."

"Huh. Well, they look all set up at least." Cobbs pans the encampments, then passes the pipe back to Holiday.

"Oh yeah. This is the place to be." Holiday slumps into another camping chair. "By the time JJ and them get over here from MO Valley, this barn'll be full up. And they'll all have to camp outside." He takes a hit.

"Good for us. Bad for them," Cobbs says. Then he points at the giant vehicles looming over their heads. "What about these? Won't we be in the way in here?"

"Nah." Holiday exhales a cloud. "They don't use these."

"Really?"

"Yeah." Holiday passes the pipe. "These were here last summer too. They haven't moved."

"Wow. That's nuts."

"Yeah. It's because these don't have the enclosed cabins."

"What?"

"These don't have those Popemobile-looking domes up top. With A/C, radio, TV and whatever. So they don't even fuck with 'em."

"Really? That's crazy."

"Yeah. Fuck 'em."

"This is some great weed by the way." Cobbs passes the pipe back to Holiday.

"Thanks. It's Blueberry."

Though accustomed to shwag doobies in cow pastures,

Cobbs is no stranger to dank ass nuggets. Weed snob—like Holiday—he is not. But, Cobbs did attend two Phish shows his freshman year. Nevertheless, eight or nine hits of this shit knocks him on his ass.

"Well, guess we better get to it," Holiday proposes, striking the bowl's ashes out against his palm.

"Let's do it," a high-flying Cobbs assents, thankful that Holiday has elected himself taskmaster.

And so our stoned protagonists circumnavigate the fleet, disembark the Ark-barn—via its spacious, Douglas fir-columned port side—and return to the Maxima. Where, with all the care of a backhoe, Holiday hoists a bundle of his gear up and out of the trunk, then waddles with it back into the barn.

Standing there at the edge of the concrete, staring at his feet, Cobbs intends to follow Holiday's lead. But this slab is really something! He can't stop admiring it. I mean, there's 7,500 square feet of cement here. Placid as a pond—despite the sloped topography. And dense as a kitchen countertop. But thicker. Way thicker. "They must've poured this for driving Paul Bunyan's farm equipment in and out of here," he speculates.

Looking up, finally, Cobbs is just as thoroughly seduced by the awning. Solid steel. Pad insulation (so no LOUD RAIN). It's a massive metal sheet lean-to that slopes down from the roof, affixed with metal bolts. Cobbs shambles along beneath it, blitzed.

Soon, he finds himself "outside." Still plenty of concrete: No surprise there. But it seems the awning had kept hidden a real Wonder of the Detasseling World! Cobbs legs excitedly up to the base of a towering contraption. Or rather, a structure? It's hard to say which—Lots of moving parts. Just what the heck is this thing? He paws an entrance to investigate.

(Reader, are you familiar with solar showers? If so, you may envision a metallic bag with a nozzled hose dangling out the bottom. Well, the da Vincis at Scranton Camp improved significantly upon that simple design. First, they replaced the bag with

35

two industrial-sized blue drums—plastic, not metal. Then they welded (melted?) those drums together. Next, as you're supposed to hang the shiny bag from a tree branch (for the sun to warm it and for gravity to later expend it), our Noah's Ark-barn artisans raised a soaring platform. Whereupon they hoisted that doubled-up blue drum reservoir and ran a hose to it. Finally, they fashioned a washroom in front of their solar-shower-tower by masting tarps around six tetherball poles—those ones with tires at the bottom so the walls needn't sag.)

Affixed to a garden hose, a metal showerhead hangs from the belly of the contraption/structure. And gently pendulates. Cobbs approaches it skeptically. The thing's got three settings. Cobbs flips its switch to "Single Spray." And warm water blasts a rope of dirt off the concrete.

He rushes back to the car, beaming. "I can't believe that's a shower over there!"

"I know, right," Holiday smirks. "That thing's fucking awesome!" Then, he drops his bundle back into the trunk. "Fuck it. Let me show you the important shit real quick."

"Cool!"

"But then we gotta make a run to the store. Before it gets too late."

"Sounds like a plan."

"Right." Holiday lights a cigarette. "So over here..."

Their tour begins with a high-powered spotlight mounted beneath the barn's north gable. "It makes a great nightlight," Holiday docents. "You hardly ever need a flashlight around here." Next, Cobbs learns that the open barn door he wanted to drive through earlier doubles as a soccer goal. Its counterpart: a thin rectangle of dirt dug into the side of that "mountain." Next up, Holiday leads Cobbs way on down to the south end of the barn. To an antique refrigerator. This thing chirps like bait shop crickets & looks like a spaceship. But it works. "For dank beers only," Holiday instructs. A far better discovery: the myriad electrical outlets running along the wall. Next, Holiday takes Cobbs outside to a spigot. "Unscrew the hose if you ever need to use this. Otherwise, leave it hooked up to the shower." Finally, Holiday steers Cobbs around the concrete slab and into the beanfield. Fifty feet out, there's one of those old-timey, red-handled well pumps sticking up out of the ground like a periscope. Cobbs lifts its vise-clamp of a handle. And cold, clear water sluices across his fingers.

"Man, this place is awesome," he exclaims.

"Damn right," Holiday grins. "Now, let's finish unloading our gear. Then go buy some beer."

"All Right!"

Part 2 - Ramen Holiday

(Okay. You've arrived, rookie Reader. Familiarized yourself with the greatest detasseling camp in human history—from which to model and/or compare your own, should the need arise. Cobbs kept things fresh. Inaugural. But the rest of this story requires you to don a hooligan's point of view. Otherwise, you'll miss out on all the whys & wherefores. Furthermore, Holiday's better suited to teach you about supplies. So, at this time I would ask that you please discard your Cobbs avatar, as we'll be shifting over to Holiday to conclude this chronicle. Indeed, and further, when we do reach its conclusion, I want you to ask yourself: What would you have done in Holiday's shoes?)

And so Holiday & Cobbs bumble & trundle... hopscotch & seesaw... pile & pitch two new mounds of Corn gear against the barn's west wall. Though they lack the hardcore guerilla gear advisable for your more destitute campsites (like MO Valley), Holiday believes they've packed the essentials. First up: Tents. Even when you're camping inside of a barn, you'll want a tent for privacy, storage, storms, bugs, etc. Holiday brought the same two-person tent he used last summer. But he added a blue tarp & some 50-50 rope for an outdoor canopy, just in case. Cobbs purchased a three-man tent at Walmart this morning as they left Arkansas. Next up: Sleep. Holiday packed his hammock (another job for those Douglas fir posts) and a swimming pool raft (still in the box) as a backup. Cobbs bought a queen-sized, inflatable air mattress at Walmart. For Cooking: Holiday shoved his camp stove, propane tanks (not the big ones!), dishes, and a few spices inside of two ice chests—his first aid kit, Camelbak (described in "Horsepower") & a half-gallon water jug fit in there too. For Clothes: They each stuffed a duffel bag, obesely, with tee shirts, shorts, socks, underwear, two pairs of pants, a jacket & a swimsuit. They'll buy their field wear at local thrift shops in the coming days—Except for work shoes! For that, Holiday packed his least favorite pair of indoor soccer shoes—comfortable and expendable. He urged Cobbs to avoid boots, particularly cowboy boots, but Cobbs may need a day in the fields to cure his obstinacy. Next up: Rec Time. Holiday brought his acoustic guitar & fourth-favorite soccer ball. Cobbs, despite Holiday's assurance that he'd never use it, brought his fishin' pole. Finally: Dank Ass Nuggets. Holiday learned last year that a good rule of thumb is one quarter per week; or, a gram a day. He's smuggled an ounce of Blueberry indica, alongside Cobbs's half pound of shwag, inside of a fireproof safe. Even rubbed Tabasco around the rims because some Deadhead (Grateful Dead) told him it would fool drug dogs.

Finished. The Maxima's trunk is empty.

Now it's twilight. The barn's nightlight floods the camp soccer pitch with a Dutch orange glow, which the moon seems poised to grind tonight beneath its pellucid white bootheel. Holiday chokes down a cigarette and stamps the butt out in the goalie box—disrespectfully, like a proper forward. Then he ducks into the barn to grab his ice chests. Meanwhile, Cobbs awaits in the car—Engine running. Probably singing, "B. Double E. Double R. U. N. BEER RUN," Holiday imagines.

Holiday hauls his two emptied coolers outside, stows them in the trunk, then circles round and opens the passenger-side door. "Damn. I'm still high as a muther fucker," he reports, oozing into his seat.

"Me too," Cobbs agrees affably.

And they make tracks. (Sorry Reader, no daredevilry upon departure—the ramp only works in one direction.) Because a detasseler hasn't finished "moving in" to Corn until they've stocked two very Corn-specific ice chests. First, there's the kitchen cooler. Even with diner breakfasts, daily, and breakneck dinners (arriving to a restaurant immediately prior to closing), nightly, each & every detasseler should maintain a cornucopian kitchen cooler. Stock it with bread, cheese, meat, veggies, fruit, orange juice, etc.—whatever you like. Just be sure to use BLOCK ICE. Could the kitchen cooler wait a day? Sure. But Corn-specific ice chest number two tends to rush detasselers to the store. As it's their beer cooler. Pro tip: buy cans. More will fit inside. Plus, you can shotgun cans should your budget require the increased efficiency. Whichever brew route you choose though, make sure to buy LOOSE ICE for your beer cooler. As cooler maintenance can dominate a detasseler's afterwork chores, there's really no good reason to delay setting them up. HOWEVER, if you've got an open safe filled to the brim with felonious marijuana sitting in your backseat, you might want to consider it!

Less than a quarter mile from camp, Holiday notices their stoney-baloney fuckup. He turns a sly eye at Cobbs: "You didn't notice that it smells like Hot Sauce and Skunk in here?"

"What?" Cobbs seems genuinely confused.

"All our weed is just sitting out, in the open, in your backseat," Holiday rephrases. Then he swings his eyes, meaningfully, in that direction.

"Oh Shit!" Cobbs's eyeballs explode.

"Yeah, oh shit! Why didn't you say something?"

"I didn't know!"

"How the hell'd you not know!? It smells like a harvest in here!"

"Dude! I'm high as fuck right now!" Cobbs yelps. And his earnest sincerity is thicker than the skunky funk he claims he never smelled.

Suddenly, like a doctor just hammered his kneecap, Holiday reflexes a smile. It's wry, but it kicks. And he starts to chuckle. Cobbs's guileless authenticity has melted Holiday's cynical hooligan heart—just a little. All his Conway friends would be lying, fiending to smoke more Blueberry nuggets as soon as possible. But not Cobbs. Cobbs is just a big-hearted boob, Holiday muses. So, rather than saying: "Whoops. Guess we better turn around." Holiday instead, caught up in the moment, says: "Ah, fuck it. It's Corn." Besides, he reflects, now they can smoke another bowl on their way to the store—as Cobbs's no-smoking-in-the-Maxima policy only applies to tobacco.

Roasting blueberries, they sally forth.

At the store, they stock their ice chests and secrete the weed safe back up under the spare tire before they leave the parking lot.

Driving back to Scranton, Holiday feels safer. More secure.

Cobbs must not be stressing it though: He starts driving way too fast. So, Holiday says as much.

"Oh come on," Cobbs complains. "We're in the middle of nowhere. Everybody's probably already back to camp by now. Gus and Hayes too." (Gus Banks & Hayes Harper are his friends from Clinton.)

"I'm just telling you," Holiday harps. "You should slow down."

Sure enough: "WHOOP WHOOP! WAAAAHHH! WHOOP WHOOP! WAAA..."

Cobbs shits his pants. Figuratively. Though literally would probably play better—due to the lingering pot smell. He starts blubbering: "Oh shit oh shit oh shit oh shit oh shit..."

Holiday tries to calm him down: "Okay dude. SHIT! Just shut the fuck up okay?"

40

"Oh fuck oh fuck oh fuck oh fuck oh fuck…" Cobbs continues, unmollified.

"You need to be cool." Holiday grabs Cobbs's arm. Firmly. "Just follow my lead. Okay?"

Frantic, Cobbs nods.

(Reader, Setting regularly features prominently in Storytelling. Thus, you've every right to wonder, "Where the hell are they?" Upon departing Scranton, did our pot-muling perps turn right on Interstate 30 to patron the grocery store in Jefferson? Or, did they turn left to client the Walmart in Carroll? Perhaps they turned right, but then drove beyond Jefferson—into Boone or Ames for better beer options? Hell, maybe they didn't turn onto Interstate 30 at all? And instead took the backroads through completely different towns? For craven legal considerations, I'm casting a wide net of suspicion here. As I've never known a police department to celebrate scrutiny. However, I refuse to ensnare Scranton in the web. For Scranton, Iowa—Greene County Emerald of the Corn Belt—is too sacrosanct; its people too industrious, warmhearted & accommodating for such aspersions. Plus, I don't believe Scranton employs a police officer here in the year 2000? In any event, now that you know I'm not just being lazy, let us return unto the scene.)

Holiday lights a cigarette. Most cars in his life already smell like tobacco smoke—it's baked into the upholstery. Which makes masking the smell of pot way easier. But not this one! Vigorously, he fumigates. But he realizes quickly it's not gonna work. This cop WILL smell their hot-boxed, left-to-linger-while-inside-the-store, blueberry bowl. So with a brave frown, Holiday takes his pipe and loose nugget out of the glovebox. And he palms them.

Meanwhile, Cobbs's legs are shaking like they're being fed into a woodchipper. But, waist-up he kind of looks still. Still enough at least.

Holiday, of course, has already snuffed his own fear & anxiety out like the cashed bowl in his hand. "Fight or Flight?"

Mere jargon for simpletons. Holiday knows you've gotta harness that adrenaline, that clarity of focus, to plan. To problem solve. To scheme. That bud vault in the trunk? Highly unlikely to bust them. Because it smells like pot *smoke* in here—not pot. Plus, the cruiser parked behind them doesn't have "K-9" displayed anywhere. And, Holiday plans to fall on his sword as a misdirection anyway. Next up, no open containers. No closed ones either—except in the trunk. And since Holiday doesn't turn twenty-one until October, the alcohol situation matters. Lastly, appearances. Holiday apprises his visage anew in the rearview mirror. Inconveniently, a mop of beeswaxed, medusoid, white-boy dreadlocks stare back at him. Aggressively. He's got the remedy though: the cult of personality. Even better, Cobbs is driving. And Cobbs looks like a young Republican.

Holiday reaches over Cobbs's convulsing legs to press the driver's side window button down. Then, once the preppy bust of Huckleberry Cobbs is on display, Holiday opens his own window. "Just follow my lead," he repeats to Cobbs, taking another drag off his cigarette.

Then they just sit there. Silent.

Finally, the officer decamps from his patrol car. And approaches. He's tall & lanky, early-thirties with a beer gut, Holiday observes. Got a neck on him too—lizardy. But it's the way he's walking that's really striking. It's wacky as fuck! Looks a lot like that passive-assertive Jesus warpath that church folks'll do sometimes when they're good & worked up. All hips & knees. Arms flailing, limp at the shoulders. Wriggly. This cop parades all the way up to Cobbs's window like that. Then, once he arrives, he doesn't even lean down. Just starts talking to the sky!

"You know why I pulled you over?" he interrogates the roof of the Maxima.

And, like a coward's bladder, Cobbs gushes: "I am s-s-so... s-s-sorry..." But mercifully, he chokes on his own sobs.

"Clocked you going nineteen over the limit," the officer continues, seemingly unaware that Cobbs just spoke. "But, now

I'm afraid... (he chooses this moment to dip his head down level with the window) You boys haven't been smoking any grass, have you?" And he stares hard at Cobbs. Then at Holiday. Then back at Cobbs. Kind of like he's saying "dun-dun-DUUUN" in his head while he's doing it.

Holiday studies the face his adversary. Sandy blond hair. Cop Mustache big as a comb. Hooded dumb cornflower eyes. Manipulatable? Definitely. This dude's one of those preening chihuahua types.

Still, Holiday knows he's going to jail. "Yes Sir," he pipes up before Cobbs can say anything stupid. "Here is *my* paraphernalia and *my* marijuana Sir." Then Holiday very slowly, very deliberately opens his palm and extends the misdemeanors into the officer's grasp.

"Well, I... Um, yes. Okay then." The officer stares at the goods in his hand. Then, without another word, he spins around and speedwackywalks back to the cruiser—his arms flapping around like one of those inflatable tube guys with a blower shoved up his ass.

Anew, Cobbs starts bawling: "Oh fuck oh fuck of fuck..."

"Just be cool," Holiday whispers soothingly. "Don't even let him see your lips moving."

Holiday puffs his cigarette. And prognosticates: Did he just purchase their freedom with a 10-dollar pipe & 20-dollar nugget? It's certainly possible. But the longer this cop sits back there, the less likely that outcome becomes. Unless he's roasting a bowl? But that'd be obvious, right?

Five minutes later, the officer alights again. And once more that wacky walk! Rubbery. Gumby-ish. Upon arrival, he leans down level to Cobbs's window straightaway this time. "Why don't you two go ahead and step out of the car."

(FUCK!!!)

"Yes sir," Holiday answers, swallowing hard. Then he very slowly, very deliberately opens the door. And exits the Maxima.

"Yes s-sir," Cobbs murmurs.

Holiday flicks his cigarette into the ditch and circles around the hood. Then he leans against the tire well, next to Cobbs.

The cop expounds: "I clocked you speeding back there. And you've fessed up to the marijuana. I appreciate that. Going just fourteen over the limit... and with your good attitudes... usually, I'd let you go with a warning. But I can't have you boys driving around out here under the influence. Simple as that."

"Oh, we understand that Sir," Holiday responds obsequiously. "That marijuana was all mine. This guy," he points at Cobbs with a thumbs-up sign, "even told me I shouldn't smoke it, but I twisted his arm. It was a long drive up here to detassel. And I got a bit impatient. I took advantage Sir."

The cop stares at Holiday. Then at Cobbs: "You mean to tell me you're not high as a kite son?"

Cobbs opens his mouth. To speak, presumably. But nothing comes out. So he clears his throat...

"MEOW! MEOW!" squeals a frizzy-haired, black-and-white tomcat (Maine Coon or Ragamuffin) while it scratches itself indulgently against the police cruiser's front bumper.

The officer's face floods crimson. "Aw hell! Goddam it!" he barks. "I fucking hate cats. Hold on a second fellas." He turns and storms back to his car—but completely normal-like! Well, he's stomping mad. But all that speedwackywalking shit vanishes into thin air. Like how a fake accent will disappear whenever shit gets real.

The cop marches down there and shoos the cat away. Then, the muther fucker just starts dancing! Legs flinging & flapping around like he's got that blower up his ass again.

Holiday can't believe his eyes. "This is fucking nuts," he whispers to Cobbs—hoping to further soothe and calm Huckleberry's nerves.

Perhaps revealing, finally, some self-consciousness, the officer tries to camouflage the last of his gyrations as shadowboxing. But then he struts back down the road like Gumby again.

"Sorry about that guys," he says. "I just—"

44

—"MEOW! MEOW!" the tomcat interrupts. It's sitting atop the cruiser this time—in front of the lightbar. Must've strafed through the field & doubled back. Pawprints polka dot the engine hood.

The cop's face drains so pale that his veins look like filaments inside a lightbulb. "GODDAM IT," he explodes—loud enough to frighten the cat away. Still, he goosesteps all the way back there anyway, then sentries around the cruiser till he's satisfied. Even lays prone to check the undercarriage.

After which of course, he speedwackywalks back to the Maxima. "Again. I'm sorry about that," he says, winded. "I just hate cats."

"Yeah. Me too," Holiday says.

"Me too," Cobbs says.

"MEOW! MEOW!" revives the tomcat, belting like a church organ.

"GOD DAMN IT! I FUCKING HATE CATS," the cop screams, abdicating his sanity.

The cat's strutting down the middle of the road now.

And the officer just leaps for it...

but he misses by a mile.

He misses so badly in fact, that the cat doesn't even run off this time. Rather, it stops and sits there crouched, cleaning itself in the median.

The cop rolls over, rubs his knees and collects himself. Then he addresses Holiday & Cobbs: "Tell you what. If one of you boys'll kick the shit out of this cat, I'll let you go."

Holiday doesn't hesitate. He's played forward on each of his soccer teams since he was six. Plus, he knows that every moment he wastes becomes a fresh opportunity for Cobbs to fuck this up.

The trick with cats, Holiday well knows, is that they try to mirror us humans. So if you want to manipulate one, you just mirror that rascal right back. Because: when you aim two mirrors at each other, the reflections will repeat themselves.

45

Infinitely. Which'll mesmerize just about any cat.

It's a quick approach: right, left, pause—Holiday really beams the cat's inner psyche back at it. Then another right. Left. No pause—

—Holiday punts that poor bastard all the way to Nebraska.

The cop jumps up cheering. Giddy. Like his side just won a war. "FUCK YEAH," he ejaculates. "You boys are free to go!" He brushes himself off, speedwackywalks back to his cruiser, and blue lights away.

Oddly enough, it's Cobbs who breaks the silence: "What the fuck just happened?"

"I don't know," Holiday says. "And I don't care. Let's get the fuck out of here."

Stunned & sapped, our heroes sidle back into the Maxima. And drive back to camp.

(So, here we are Reader. The End. Now be honest, what would you have done in Holiday's shoes? Put to task, would you opt for easy freedom? Or incarcerating principles? I know what I'd have done: I'd have kicked that cat. But what's your own verdict? That's what's important here. It's hard to know for sure, isn't it? Might be wise to stay away from this line of work—corn detasseling that is—lest you're prepared for such revealing tests of character.)

Drunken Kickball
End of Season Party (2001)
– Official Rules –

1. Same rules as Drunken Wiffle Ball, as amended herein.

2. **Kegs.** You'll need three (at least): two for the infield & one in center field fifteen feet behind second base, aligned with home plate.

3. **Defense.** Placement of the *infield* kegs is discretionary, so long as they don't block the basepaths. Additionally, the fielding team may reconfigure these infield kegs prior to each new kicker. (Though more than two infield kegs are permitted, most pundits agree that extras serve best as iced-down, on-the-ready replacements.) Finally, illegal outs (to the head or neck) are prohibited. Baserunners' cups of beer, however, are both strikable and taggable (constituting part of the body).

4. **Offense.** Aiming the kickball at the kegs, like pinball bumpers, is Drunken Kickball's cornerstone: dominating offensive strategies... eliciting defensive repositionings... and on and on and on. Importantly, if the ball ricochets off any two kegs, in any order, it constitutes a homerun. (Thus requiring a keg stand via the precedent jurisprudence of Drunken Wiffle Ball, Rule 2.)

5. There is no debate in Drunken Kickball: players *must* pause the game in pursuance of *all* keg stands. Non-stop injuries in the Sport's formative years coalesced a uniform opinion: WATCH OUT!

6. Steel buckets, or similar objects, should protect the keg taps.

7. The game ends when the kickball starts flopping around like a jellyfish. (Two backups are permissible.)

Corn Soundtracks

Working Corn facilitates comradery & friendships. If you pair up to split blocks, the workday will breeze on by. But maybe you'd rather maximize your moolah? If so, I recommend shuttin' the fuck up & listening to your Corn Soundtracks.

"Okay," you say. "But what the hell are Corn Soundtracks?" Allow me to explain, from the bottom up.

My own Corn Soundtracks were the best albums in my travel CD case that didn't skip, stop, or otherwise flounder inside my Sony Discman while I galloped through cornfields. Corn Soundtracks for Ramen Holiday were 80-minute Mini-Disc mixes he pirated off Napster. Huckleberry Cobbs's Corn Soundtracks were CD copies of Holiday's MiniDiscs. Corn Soundtracks have also existed as cassette tapes, digital music libraries & mere radios.

Still, the term Corn Soundtrack denotes a broader concept than this mere edict: "Listen to music while you're detasseling." Sure, that's the nitty gritty mechanics of Corn Soundtracks. But it lacks a vital component. Detasselers literally walk marathons (sometimes daily) listening to this music. And that immersion, that seeming monotony, grows (eventually) into Corn Soundtracks' coolest feature: the music will forever whisk its listeners back into the cornfields!

These days, my own Corn Soundtracks (i.e., *Are You Gonna Go My Way*; *Traveling Without Moving*; *The Bends*; *Smash*; *What Hits!?*; *40oz. to Freedom*; *The Carnival*; *New Morning*) have become retro chic—garnering regular PA play at my local grocery stores, bookstores, thrift shops... all & sundry hotspots. If their employees can just stay off that damned intercom, the aisles will metamorphose into rows of corn as I prestidigitate back into Arcadia. Still, *my* Corn Soundtracks won't help you, Dear Reader. You'll have to forge your own. Otherwise, they won't ripen into fountains of youth/teleportation devices.

The Tasseltown Debacle

Or *Workplace Etiquette*

Politics. Lots of people love the stuff. Me? I figured it out a while ago: Right-wingers are Chimpanzees, Left-wingers are Bonobos, and nobody can spot an ape. So, nowadays I focus that lens on more utilitarian topics: like office politics.

Now, I know what you're thinking: "Why would I listen to this guy's opinions on etiquette?" For I too have read the pages preceding this one. But here's the thing: I'm going to teach you exactly what NOT to do in Corn. We'll review my myriad faux pas, which'll leave *you* poised to abide decorum. Trust me, this'll work. See, my sixth (& final) year of Corn (2005), I broke every rule in the book. I went full-on antihero.

But first, a quick note for potential crew bosses. It's traditional to rent a house in your host town for the detasseling season. In 2005 Tasseltown, however, Bob & Mona Sturgis rented two. I lived in the smaller residence, uptown, with three other people. The larger house, downtown, billeted twelve feral males. Theirs was a rattrap, but it dilapidated conveniently across the street from the local bar. The remaining thirty or so detasselers, including Bob & Mona, camped in a barren field two miles west of town. As Tasseltown proper featured but twenty residences, one diner, said watering hole, a post office & a Casey's gas station/convenience store, the sensitive Reader may well imagine the degree to which the Tasseltownies felt besieged...

Ssss . . . PunNCKT! Ssss . . . PunNCKT! Ssss . . . PUNCKT!
Talking to myself: "Nebraska. FUCKING NEBRASKA! What the fuck? These aren't tassels—they're ROOTS! Fuck this. I'm smoking a bowl."

I fish my Ziplocked pot out of my pocket and pack a spoonful of dank. Then I rip it like a brushfire.

A tassel whizzes past my ear. "Hey! I'm smoking over here!"
"No shit, Asthmatazz," my assailant ribs. "That cough of
yours's notorious." It's Heath Phillips (whom I mentioned in
"Horsepower"), a veteran from Wisconsin and presently one of
my roommates at the smaller rental house.

"Oh, hey Heath. What's up? Care to partake?"

"Uh, yeah." Heath parts an entrance through the corn rows
& sits down in the dirt next to me. Bandanas cover his head &
neck, but Heath's face, as usual, remains fully exposed. Heath's
long fancied himself a Gavin Rossdale clone, so he never covers
his visage—even out here amongst the Corn.

I pack a fresh bowl and hand it over, asking, "You and Wendy want to go in on another 30-pack tonight?" Wendy Stone
is Heath's longtime, on-again-off-again girlfriend. (Currently
off-again, importantly.) She too hails from Wisconsin and lives
with us at the rental house.

Heath takes a rip. "Nah. She says she wants to go to the bar
tonight. Play some pool."

"Right on. I'll be over that way too. Dallas twisted my arm
into playing poker."

"I thought you hated poker?"

"Yeah."

"Why'd you agree to play then?"

"Public Relations? I don't know... maybe Lillie Gillespie will
show up?" I laugh. (Let me fill you in Reader: "Lillie Gillespie"
is an alias we'll be using to protect the identity of a real life popstar! Here in 2005, she's a headliner. So going forward, whenever you see "Lillie Gillespie," you should think: "Not Madonna;
but bigger than Sarah MacLauchlan." Just five days ago, fellow
detasseler Stephen Barnes—Dallas's best friend & current roommate at the other rental house—shocked our whole crew by
claiming he hooked up with her. Five years ago. Pre-fame. Once.
In his college dorm room. In case it isn't obvious, the lesson here
Reader is never kiss and tell in Corn. Firstly, gossip spreads like
earworms in a cornfield. Secondly, there's no guarantee some

50

muther fucker won't publish your secrets twenty years later.)

"Ha!" Heath snorts. "Lying ass Barnes... Bet you can take those dudes for some money though."

"Maybe."

Heath offers my pipe back, but I wave it off. So he takes another rip. Then he looks down at his feet for a while before saying, "Hey man, I wanted to let you know that I apologized to Bob and Mona this morning... for yesterday."

"Really?"

"Yeah. They said everyone's been coming up to them. They're calling it 'The Angry Day.' Kind of dismissing it like that... you know. Maybe you should talk to them too?"

"Why?"

"Well, you did shout to all of Nebraska that the Seed Company played them for fools... among other things. You even said you wished you hadn't come out here this year. Plus, all that negativity spread around the crew... People look up to us."

"Ah hell, we were just blowing off steam."

"We were being assholes," Heath says firmly. "And everybody heard us."

"Oh c'mon. Every field we've worked out here has been worse than the one that came before. That's just reality. But we're supposed to smile and pretend to be happy about it? That's bullshit. So we said some mean shit—So what? People say mean shit all the time. Usually, it all just floats away. But Bob and Mona decided they'd lay down and hide in their truck— eavesdropping on everybody. Without them spying on us, this wouldn't even be a thing."

Heath takes another lungful of smoke. "Huh. That kind of makes sense."

"We didn't do anything wrong man."

"Right... Well, I'm stoned. Better get back to it," he says, returning my glass piece.

"Right on. See you tonight."

"Thanks for the bud." Heath disappears back into the maize.

Talking to myself again: "Welp. Back to work. This row's looking a smidge better. Way to go Cornhuskers! You drove a tractor straight for ten whole feet... aaaaaaand it's back to bullshit!" That didn't take long. Wait a minute. I think I understand now: Nebraskans have Corn Envy. Hell, they're probably tortured by it. Their neighbor, Iowa, comprises America's fertile crescent—it's a real cradle of civilization over there. Then, you take a left at the taint and here's Nebraska: Iowa's left butt cheek. You know, I bet if it wasn't for us migrants pulling twenty fields worth of tassels out of every goddam block of corn, this whole State would starve to death. "FUCK YOU, NEBRASKA!"

I abandon my block of corn. There's Nicotine gum in my Jeep, and I aim to chew it.

Should've looked before storming off though—Bob's at the front of the field!

I stroll down the dusty berth between the panels and the buffer zone like nothing's up. Real quiet. Lamb-like.

Bob doesn't seem to notice me. He's too preoccupied watching the crew: 40-odd kaleidoscopic hats & bandanas zipping up and down the rows like beads on an abacus. I've witnessed this hawkeyed captain's pose of Bob's many times: his "thousand-cob stare." Usually, it means he's busy/don't bother him.

"Hey JJ," Bob detonates, without so much as a flinch in my direction.

(SHIT!!!)

"Hey Bob," I bleat. And my legs stop moving.

Two seconds of stillness ensue. Me: catatonic. Bob: iron-willed.

Finally, Bob turns his head... ever so slightly. And he's smiling! Nothing's wrong! See, I knew Heath was overreacting. Bob's a man's man. Big ass mustache. Drinks scotch. Smokes cigars. Rides a Harley! Why bring up old shit with a guy like Bob? He'd probably just laugh in my face.

"Ran out of my nicotine gum," I say. "Got more in the car."

"Okay," Bob chuckles, and returns his gaze to the field.

My legs start working again, so I bolt.

And not ten seconds later, here comes Mona driving their extra-wide Dodge Ram dually/stakeout-mobile, barreling right at me.

(SHIT!!!)

I consider knifing through the buffer zone, but decide it'd look too suspicious. So, I soldier onward, my gait & bearing all the more ovine.

Mona parks ten feet in front of me! And of course, she's smiling too. Mona looks like a hippiefied Meryl Streep, beaming sunnily. "Well hello JJ," she says, alighting. "You doing all right today?" Then she beetles around the driver's side to her tailgate—to pour fresh water for their rough-and-tumble mastiffs, Zena and Molly.

Zena, the tawny adult Bullmastiff, leaps over the hatch quick as Mona touches the handle. Meanwhile Molly, the rhino-gray adolescent Neapolitan, wishes desperately she could mimic Zena. But Molly's clumsy. And she knows it. And so does Zena.

"Oh. Hi Mona." I lean down to pet Zena before she gambols off. "Yeah, I'm fine. Just need some more nicotine," I *say*. But what I'm *thinking* is, "I know you hope to add mine to your day's collection of shame-faced apologies. But I am a rock."

"You want an American Spirit?" Mona indicates the tobacco pouch heaping from her back pocket.

"Oh no. No thanks. I don't smoke cigarettes anymore. I'm on the gum."

"Really?! That's great. Good for you!"

Our conversation thus straddles the razor's edge.

"Thanks. Well, I'd better go," I peep, and hasten away.

"See you later," Mona cries.

Once I'm safely out of range, I turn to smile goodbye.

Mona's not looking though. She's helping an oafish, 80-pound puppy disembark from the tailgate.

53

Meanwhile, Zena's already sitting next to Bob. Who feeds her bacon.

Back at my Jeep, I pop two pieces of Nicotine gum & turn the engine on to listen to music. 'Ramblin' Man' starts playing. I chomp that gum till it's a wad of peppery putty, watching all the kooky abacas beads slide up and down the cornfield.

Then, I drive into Tasseltown for a can of Copenhagen.

(Rapt & sympathetic-to-the-follies-of-youth Reader, out of all the Corn etiquette I've violated in the past few pages, my departure from the field tops them all. "Till the Field is Done," is a detasseler's most sacred battle cry.)

There's an empty Gatorade bottle sitting atop the gas pump garbage can. So I snag it for a spitter and jump back into my Jeep, brown bagging two forties & tin of longcut from Casey's. Buzzing & humming Allman Brothers, I drive across town to our rental house—three blocks away.

No one's home of course. There were still 50 blocks left unclaimed when I went AWOL, so I should enjoy a couple hours to myself here. I reverse my Jeep's tailgate up to the front porch and hop out to unload my gear. Afterwards, I slink into the green plastic lawn chair that came furnished on the porch & scrape my shoes off against my beer cooler/ottoman. Then I just sit there in the shade, sprawled like viscous goo...

and fall asleep.

When I awaken, it's twilight. The moon lurks behind some clouds—its glow a deep sable. Indeed, tonight's moon looks a lot like the wad of Copenhagen that's now stuck to my shirt. I check the clock on my piece-of-shit Nokia cellphone: "//8~:4`7," it reads.

Thankfully, none of my roommates are home yet. So I sprint to the bathroom.

My three roommates: Heath, Wendy & Julian—a veteran from Kentucky, peal into the house just as I'm finishing up.

"You didn't use all the hot water, did you!" Heath shouts through the bathroom door.

"No way," I answer. "Left it all for you guys!"

"So kind. So kind," he says.

(This repartee is all in jest of course. None of us takes hot showers. Warmish? Yes. But during Corn, a hot shower feels like diving into a patch of nettles, full of wasps. Still, every detasseler covets a shower at the end of a workday. Thus, "You didn't use all the hot water, did you!" actually means "Get out of the shower please.")

When I open the bathroom door, Heath's still standing there. Leaning up against the frame—All up in my face!

And I won't lie, Heath can be a scary dude. By all rights, I *should* be nervous: it'd be reasonable for him to be mad at me for leaving the field early. Plus, there's all that Angry Day business. Then again, you never know with Heath. Could be he's just mad I didn't scoop him up when I split.

Lucky for me, Heath can't keep up his ruse. "So... kind?" He breaks into a smile. Then he reveals, from behind his back, his glass bubbler—a pink & purple masterpiece named "Dragon Punch." And it's stuffed to the brim with dank ass nuggets! (No bowl is more important than the after work, back-at-camp/back-at-the-rental-house bowl Reader. In times of scarcity, ALWAYS prioritize this end-of-the-day ritual. For it revitalizes & rejuvenates more than any other. Also, it strengthens communal bonds.)

With alacrity, the four of us consolidate into the front den—"The Dude Room." For seats, Heath grabs his beer cooler, I drag my duffel bag, Julian stacks some pillows, and Wendy appropriates that tranquilizing lawn chair from off the porch. Thusly, we squeeze into a circle under the ceiling fan. Heath tenders Dragon Punch. I load my spoon. Wendy packs her sherlock. And round and round we go...

55

After we cash those bowls, Julian reloads Dragon Punch
with some of his homegrown—
SHORUKEN!

—and that really gets the job done.

Stoned silence settles upon us like a lead balloon. So, anti-
dote-ically I chirp, "Welp! Guess I've got a poker game to get
to!" Which pulls us all back from the brink.

As I close the front door, a collective "Bye!" wafts from the
stirring figures within. Behind me, my beer cooler awaits.

"Hello," it yawns.

Goblet in hand, I descend into a dark & starless night—

lamped in naught but the Copenhagen-hued moonlight. And as I traipse across Tasseltown, I can't help but to reflect that the nighttime part of Corn has always been way better than its daytime complement.

I bust in their back door like I own the place.

And "Jay-Jay!" erupts from stem to stern: from the pot-hungry jackals seated here round the kitchen table; to the troop of baboons sharing a bathroom; to the wolfpack chugging beers in the front den.

"WHAT'S UP, MUTHER FUCKERS!" I megaphone back at 'em.

And this seems to strike the right chord. For the housemates resume their pre-"Jay-Jay!" amusements just as rapidly as they'd paused them.

To wit: the five pot-hungry jackals foam at the mouth for more poker. The frothiest of 'em's Dallas Hide, a force majeure out of Austin, Texas (founding member of Merle Beaver's herd—See "Horsepower"). Dallas's holding a deck of cards with a clenched iron fist. Next to Dallas sits Stephen Barnes, Dallas's BFF from Texas. Again, Barnes is the guy who claims he hooked up with popstar Lillie Gillespie. Presently, Barnes is crouching behind one of those gaudy poker chip briefcases, looking like an accountant. Next to Barnes sits Benjy Basil, a second-year detasseler from Columbus, Ohio. Next to Benjy sits Eric LeMayhew, a five-timer/former crew boss from Northwest Arkansas—my home State. And finally, sitting next to LeMayhew is Phoenix Fulmer, a train-hopping, peripatetic graybeard from parts unknown. Fulmer has clearly detasseled before. Indeed, he deserves his seat here amongst the horses. But for some reason, Fulmer claims he's a rookie. Even though none of the rest of us gives a shit anyway. (There's always one or two of these sphinxlike frauds on any given Corn crew Reader. Lies upon lies upon lies. Makes the rest of us seem honest, by comparison. It's usually best just to allow 'em their secrets.)

"Y'all been playing long?" I ask the table.

"Nah," Dallas chafes, frothy as a keg bottom.

"Cool," I reply smoothly. "How's the Flop House?"

"Fucking kids," he grumbles.

"We got room for you over at the Penthouse," I offer.

"Or, you could move in over here," he counters. "With your mountain of pot." And his face twitches nastily.

"Goddam. You jonesing buddy?"

"Some of us actually worked today."

Then Barnes chimes in: "Yeah, what happened to you today?"

"C'mon guys. I was just spreading the wealth around."

The table explodes in *Snorts, Pshaws, & What-do-you-take-me-fors.*

So, I strengthen my argument: "Tell you what. Whoever floats me some beers while I'm here..." I lay my pre-packed pipe on the tabletop. "Gets the green hit."

LeMayhew's beer cooler sweat-streaks from under the table at me like a hovercraft.

"Arkansas for the win," I say—foot-saving the craft from colliding with the backdoor.

"Indeed," he agrees—wasting no time in retrieving his prize.

"Anybody got another pipe?"

"This one's clean as fuck," Dallas answers me, chillum in hand. "Smoked up all the resin."

"Well let's gunk it up again." I hand him my last bud of Julian's homegrown.

Dallas breaks off a piece and packs his pipe. Then, he barbecues that poor nugglet like it's Texas brisket. Muther Fucker's sucking down hot ash & cinders before I can even get the cash out of my wallet to buy poker chips.

"That's Kentucky's finest right there," I advise. "So go easy. I don't know if Julian's willing to trade any more of it."

"That's Julian the acid-causality we're talking about?" Dallas mocks.

"Don't let him fool you. That dude's a weed hawk."

"Room for me over at the Penthouse, eh?" Dallas severs a second nugglet.

I toss Barnes a twenty, and he slides me a stack of chips. All of them have stickers that read "No-Limit Texas Hold 'Em." On both sides. I take my seat between Dallas & Fulmer and notice the lid of Barnes's briefcase has the same logo—embossed in silver dots.

Dallas reloads his chillum, then announces "The game's No-Limit Texas Hold 'Em" while he passes the pipe to Barnes.

"Yeah. No shit," I laugh, pointing at the stickers.

"Blinds are set," Dallas continues unhindered. ("Blinds" are like antes in this game.) "Let's play."

(So in case you're unfamiliar Reader, No Limit Texas Hold 'Em evolved out of seven-card stud. Everything's bigger in Texas right? Characteristically, they designed No Limit Hold 'Em to foster jumbo-sized wagering. Any round, any player can go "All In"—thus risking their entire bankroll. Here in 2005, No Limit Texas Hold 'Em has recently usurped all other poker iterations across these United States. Used to be folks played all sorts of poker. But nowadays, apparently, you can't even buy a set of normal poker chips. Fucking Texans—a plague of publicists, the lot of 'em. And from the get-go too: "Remember the Alamo." Unfortunately, these are just the kinds of people you'll have to learn to countenance should you choose to become a corn detasseler.)

We play a few hands without any fireworks. Beer buzzes bloom. Comradery coalesces. Still, I feel increasingly restless. That's why I hate poker by the way: it's boring as hell. It's like fishing—fun to catch something, but most of the time you're just sitting around with your thumb up your ass.

But then Benjy deals me a pair of Queens. And I'm reeled back in.

First action's on me. Now, conventional wisdom says to bet

big when you're dealt a high pair (these are called your "hold cards," by the way—because they're the only two your opponents can't see). But of course, I've never been too conventional. So I mutter "Check" like I haven't seen a good pair of hold cards all night.

"Check," Dallas barks.

Barnes looks around frothily, like he's dying to bet... but then he checks.

"Check," Benjy moans.

"Check," LeMayhew groans.

"Fold," Fulmer fiats & slams his cards down.

"You're the big blind," Barnes seethes. "You can just check and see the flop for free."

"F.O.L.D." Fulmer repeats.

"Whatever," Barnes says.

"Pot's right?" After a perfunctory pause, Benjy "burns" a card (discards), then he deals the next three from the deck, center-table faceup. (This is called "The Flop.")

(Being as how these cards are used by each player, the three beauts you see "flopped" above are called "Community Cards.")

"Check," I sigh, card-sharking.

"Check," Dallas huffs.

"Three dollars!" Barnes woofs.

(Okay Reader. When another player bets big like this, post-Flop, it's natural to get anxious and start pining, "Oh Shit! Am I beat? Perhaps I should doublecheck my hold cards? Maybe I didn't flop four Queens like I think." But you've got to fight that urge. Drink more beer. Smoke more pot. If it helps, remember that Poker was boring as hell till just a second ago.)

"Goddam it!" Benjy protests, flailing around like Barnes just slapped him in his face. But then, Benjy calls.

"Fold," Eric mopes.

"See?" Fulmer nods imperiously.

"Fuck it. I'll call," I grumble.

"I'm out," Dallas whines. "But I think Barnes is bluffing." (This comment ain't worth diddly-squat of course. Them two's in cahoots.)

"Pots right?" Benjy waits for objections. When none come, he burns another card, then turns over the fourth Community Card. (This one's called "The Turn," coincidentally).

My four Queens have now become unbeatable. The only poker hands stronger than four-of-a-kind are straight flushes. And (with only one card to go) none of those remain possible.

"Check," I say. Nonchalant.

"Four dollars!" Barnes boy-howdies, rising up out of his chair like an asshole.

"God dammit," Benjy growls. "I'm out."

I stare at the four Community Cards. Then up at Barnes— who's looming over the kitty like a vulture. Then, I stare at the cards again. Then up at Barnes. Then the cards. Barnes. And I keep it up until he sits his ass down. Then I thumb at my hold cards like I'm gonna sneak a peek. I don't, obviously, but I put on a good show. Finally, I relent: "Fuck it. I'll call." And I toss in my chips.

"Pot's right?" Benjy pauses, burns a card, then overturns the final Community Card. (Called "The River," for some Texafied reason.)

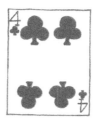

Much as I knew they would, my four Queens have survived unscathed. "I check."

"Five dollars," Barnes booms, trickling his chips into the pot like some Wild West outlaw.

And that's when it hits me: Holy Shit! Barnes really *did* hook up with Lillie Gillespie! Naturally, I just assumed he was lying. But now the truth has been revealed. This is just what Barnes looks like when he's high on himself. Poor bastard's got no poker face at all. God, it's fucking hideous. All puffed up like a bullfrog. Like he's about to tongue-spear a horsefly. Guess it takes all kinds in this world, huh? Fucking Barnes has got the goods: he flopped a boat (full house)—eights over queens. May as well've told me so.

I could clean him out. Hell, I probably should. But I feel bad—Guilty about the Lille Gillespie thing. "I guess I'll call," I say, chagrined. Expiating.

Ordinarily, when you're the one who calls, you show your cards first. But froggy Barnes doesn't give me the chance. Immediately he hops back up and crows, "Read 'em and weep," all corny-like.

"Nice hand," I say. Then I toss my Queens over his Eights—

—and they land pretty square, too.

Catatonia grips the room. Ten times more lead-balloony than Dragon Punch. Nevertheless, I won't have to antidote this spell. Minds will catch up to reality in 3... 2... 1...

UPROARIOUS JUBILATION! The whole table whoop-ees & hoots & dances & hugs. It's a madhouse in here. Atheists praise Deities. Arkansans and Texans embrace, feeling more like cousins than rivals, if only temporarily. Prodigals reminisce warmly on their fathers. Even Fulmer's high-fiving everybody.

Of course, that's all assuming you ain't Barnes at this hoo-tenanny. That dude hasn't moved. He's still staring down at the cards, like a statue.

I guess finally sensing me eyeballing him, Barnes looks up & says, "I thought I had you."

I shrug, grinning like an asshole.

Eventually, we all simmer down and fish out fresh beers.

Barnes surveys his dwindled stack of chips. "You could've cleaned me out." And there's that bullfrog grin of his sneaking back up.

I nod & smile indulgently. Then I ask him to cash me out, hoping nobody gets mad I'm taking all this loot out of circula-tion.

But I needn't worry...

Because a primal shriek sends a tremor through the Flop-house! From outside, it thunderbolts across the east wall—den to kitchen—then sirens into the backyard. And beyond...

"What the fuck was that?" Benjy gasps.

"Sounds like a raccoon fighting an alley cat," Fulmer says.

We all laugh at him, albeit nervously.

"Only one way to find out," I say, advancing to the back-door.

"I'm coming too," Dallas says, doffing his cowboy hat.

(Being from Arkansas, I've heard my fair share of racoon/cat tussles. You know how a power saw sounds once you've cut through the wood—when the blade accelerates, wildly? Well, that's the ululating you'll hear when a cat's getting fucked up by a raccoon. This commotion, unfortunately, sounds far more human.)

Indeed, upon inspection, Dallas & I discover that the shrieking tones match the upper register of our crewmate Sage Sugarfield's silky baritone. Wending about the neighborhood's flower gardens, sheds, clotheslines, sweetgums, elms & oaks, Sugarfield jackrabbits across every backyard in Tasseltown, banshee-wailing. After which, he stops at the edge of town—a bit too near the Penthouse in my opinion—and turns around beneath a convenient streetlight. "Bad Moon... w-w-white again," he bawls. "B-bad m-m-moon... GLYCERINE!" After which, he falls into the shadows and bids a silent retreat astride the highway.

Dallas & I nearly give ourselves hernias laughing so hard. And therefore, we fail to see the next-door neighbor standing out on his back deck grunting like an orangutan.

Once we're un-keeled-over though, we do notice that there's a beer-bellied King Louie snarling at us.

"You met this guy?" I ask.

"Hell no."

"Well... C'mon."

We walk a few steps over into the guy's yard, and he starts bouncing around like a beachball.

"A little jumpy," I whisper, arm-barring Dallas's path forward.

We pause.

Then I say to King Louie: "Good Evening Sir. How goes it?"

"YOU JUST STAY THE HELL AWAY FROM MY HOUSE!" he rages, swinging his arms hither thither.

Dallas & I let slip a couple titters before we can stop ourselves.

Regrettably, King Louie hears us loud & clear. He pounds a resentful retreat across his deck, then slams his backdoor shut.

"What a dickhead," I say.

"Got that right." Dallas nods.

"How would you feel," Fulmer says, surprising us both with his presence, "if some skuzzy stranger walked into *your* house?"

Dallas & I stare back at him slack-jawed.

"Whose fucking side are you on Fulmer!" we yell at him. Prompting Fulmer to shrug, condescendingly, and return to the Flophouse.

Still, he does get my wheels spinning. "Somebody should probably call Bob (Sturgis) and let him know what happened," I say to Dallas. (Indeed Reader, since mishaps, misadventures & hijinks are inevitable amongst detasselers, your crew boss will serve as your de facto liaison & diplomat with the townies.)

"I'll do it," Dallas says.

"Thanks. And thanks for the backup too."

"Anytime."

"Well. If you need me, I'll be spending Barnes's money at the bar."

"Asshole."

"Yeah yeah. Drop in for a beer later. On me."

"Too fucking loud in there."

Dallas retires to what's left of his poker game, while I cross Main Street and dive into the local tavern: "Tasseltown Taps."

(If you've seen one rural Cornbelt bar, well-traveled Reader, you've seen them all. Cash register on the nearest end of the bar top, electronic gaming box on the far end. Jukebox hugging the back wall—stocked with Country, Rock, and four Pop songs; its volume cranked to eleven. A few tables scattered helter-skelter across a floor of peanut shells. Bathroom's down a narrow hall. And that's it for the front room.

In the backroom—an annex—you'll find a coin-operated, felt-top pool table sitting beneath either a Budweiser or Coors light fixture. Without fail, it's either Clydesdales or the Rocky Mountains. Beneath the pool table's legs, cardboard coasters will strive valiantly to keep the top level. The pool cues you'll find hanging on the wall. All of them warped. Also, the walls will sport various bar ephemera: broadsides for concerts from the 60s & 70s, placards quoting off-color adages, squiggly-lined neon signs, Etc. Most importantly, for our purposes, this backroom's where you'll find corn detasselers should any be in the neighborhood. Happily, such is the case right now.)

Heath, Wendy, and a couple of rookies I haven't met yet are playing a game of doubles. Well, they were. The game's currently on hiatus while Wendy reads the riot act to Heath. She's fucking pissed. Heath keeps drooping his head lower & lower. And those rookies look like they want to crawl under the table.

Me personally though, I'm on cloud nine. So, I figure I'll brighten the mood. Hell, they're my roommates after all. I shamble up the ramp that adjoins the rooms and pretend I don't notice the fight. "Hey guys," I shout above the din of Johnny Cash's 'Burning Ring of Fire.' "Y'all catch Sugarfield running and screaming through town just now? Fucking hilarious."

Wendy spins around on me, and her black eyebrows morph into blades—aimed at my jugular! All of a sudden I'm Puglsey to her Wednesday Addams. "What happened," she demands icily.

"You mean you didn't hear?" I filibuster.

"YOU CAN'T HEAR SHIT IN HERE!"

"Oh. Yeah. I guess you're right," I say to my feet.

Then she grabs my arm and digs a single, sharp fingernail into my skin. "What. Fucking. Happened. To. Sage?" She squeezes.

And I sing: "Okay. So we were playing poker at the Flophouse, you know. And there was this shrill wailing outside. Screaming like mad. Moving fast, too—from the front of the house to the back. So we go to investigate: Me and Dallas. And it turns out it's Sugarfield! He's yelling just as loud as Johnny Cash in here and weaving in and out of everybody's backyards. Then, near our house he stops, spins around and cries, 'Bad Moon White Again! Glycerine!' Just like that Bush song."

Wendy turns her eyebrow-blades back on Heath now—which suits me fine. But then her goddam fingernail starts stabbing me worse.

I continue: "That's when Dallas and I notice the next-door neighbor's standing on his back deck, shitting a brick. He's mad as hell. Fulmer seems to think that Sugarfield walked into this neighbor guy's house and got chased off."

Wendy murders Heath with her eye-blades, then turns back around on me. "Where is Sage now?" she stabs, breaking the skin.

"Probably still running down the highway," I wince.

Her interrogation complete, Wendy releases me, chugs her beer in one gulp, then instructs Heath to pay her tab. Next she shouts "ASSHOLES!" louder than Johnny Cash's "burns, burns, burns," and marches out of the bar.

Heath & I just stand there, still as corpses.

Those two rookies? Neither one of 'em says a word. They spear their pool sticks into the wall rack then shuffle down the ramp and out the door—but careful to give Wendy a sizable head start.

Finally I turn to Heath. "What the hell am I missing here?"

"They're dating," he says.

"Who? Wendy and Sugarfield?"

"Yeah. Apparently it's been going on for a couple days."

"Oh... Shit man. I'm sorry."

"Yeah... thanks."

"Probably just a Corn hookup."

"I don't know..." Heath shakes his head droopily. "I think I really fucked things up."

"Can't be that bad?"

"I pushed him."

"You mean... physically?"

"Yeah."

"Ah." I grimace.

"She told me they were dating..."

"...and you reacted poorly?"

"Yes."

"And then Sugarfield... He just ran away?"

"Yes."

"But Wendy stayed here with you?"

"She wanted to yell at me."

"Huh. I don't know man. That's weird. They're dating, but he runs away from her—

"—from me," Heath amends.

"Okay," I concede. "And then Wendy stays here with you?"

"She wanted to straighten me out. Put an end to it."

"Maybe... Aw hell, it's none of my business."

(Corn Romances will flower and wither upon their own schedules, tender-hearted Reader. Their rhyme & reason as dizzying as their volatility. It's best not to analyze. Even bester not to interfere.)

Silence.

"Shots?" I propose.

"Sure."

We descend the ramp.

All the tables in the front parlour are packed with locals. So Heath & I grab two stools at the bar.

"Hey, you got any (Wild) Turkey!" I ask the bartender—who looks like a human cigarette.

"Just the 101!" he rasps.

"Four shots of that then," I order. "And a bucket of beer please!"

"Coming up!"

(While it *is* good office politics to spread your hard-earned detasseling bucks around your host town Reader, try not to get shit-faced at the local pubs. Townies are small town people with a whole different culture than you'll be experiencing on your Corn crew. Though the bartenders will usually put up with a lot of shit, the local patrons WILL NOT.)

I nudge Heath in the ribs. "Oh shit, I almost forgot! Turns

out Barnes really did hook up with Lillie Gillespie!"

"Bullshit," he says. But I can tell he's interested.

For the next half hour, we booze it up pretty hard.

Finally, Heath starts expectorating: "I just saw red. Sugarfield put his hand on my shoulder. Sitting here now, I can't imagine he meant anything by it. But I just fucking lost it..."

"Pretty tone deaf, I'd say," I counsel. "I mean, read the room Sugarfield."

"Yeah. I guess," Heath frowns. "Fuck! Wendy's through with me for good this time."

"What? No way. You guys are like Ross and Rachel (from *Friends*)."

"I fucking hate that show."

"Yeah me too. Anyways, Sugarfield's from South Bend, Indiana, right? You and Wendy live in the same town. In far-off Wisconsin. I bet she won't even remember his name in a couple months."

"I don't know man. She almost left me for good over my temper a couple years ago."

"But you barely pushed him. Once. And then you stopped—which to me is the crucial point here. But he runs away anyway? From Wendy too. That's gotta play in your favor right?"

"I guess," Heath says skeptically.

"Good thing *this* muther fucker didn't see anything," I say, pointing at the bartender to flag him down.

The human cigarette returns.

"Two more shots and another bucket (of beer) please!" I request amiably.

"Coming up!" he replies.

'I Walk the Line,' 'Cocaine Blues,' 'Man in Black,' 'Riders in the Sky' and an encore of 'Ring of Fire' rattle the glassware before Heath's Cash queue finally runs out—he'd dumped five bucks into the machine.

Then some local starts jamming Journey: 'Wheel in the Sky,' 'Separate Ways,' 'Any Way You Want It,' 'Don't Stop Believin'.'

Couple bars into 'Open Arms,' an electric breeze blows in through the front door. I glance up at a young couple. Definitely locals—I can tell because nobody's looking at 'em sideways. The girlfriend notices me & smiles. Double dimples.

Then she walks right up to me & Heath at the bar, followed by the boyfriend. "Hi, I'm Mandy," she says. "And this is my boyfriend Dan. Are you guys detasselers?"

(Though it's always best to avoid interacting with the locals, Reader, you definitely don't want to be rude. If you do find yourself confronted, try to be friendly & polite. But don't let your guard down either.)

"Yes Ma'am," I say. "We're drinking wishkey."

"That's great," she giggles.

"My buddy's bummed," I say.

Heath nods, frowny-face-pouty-lipped.

"Oh. I'm so sorry," she says. And I can tell that she means it.

"Great ta meecha," I say. "Shots?"

"Hey, thanks fella!" Boyfriend Dan torpedoes his arm in to shake my hand. "Daniel Newton," he says.

"JJ." We shake. "And thish ish Heash."

"Bishabosh," Heath waves.

Then I turn to the bartender: "May I've former shots? Turn-key, pleece?"

The human cigarette obliges.

"CHEERS!!!!"

"It's nice to finally meet some detasselers," Mandy says, lips freshly patinaed in iridescent whiskey-dew.

"Thanks," I say. "You wanna shum shum pool?"

"Oh, no. Sorry," she laments. "We're just dropping by. Gotta get back to Dan's parent's house soon."

"Oh... Okey."

"Maybe some other time?" she proposes.

"Shurr."

"Thanks for the shots."

"No prollum."

"Nice meeting you JJ," she smiles. "You too Heath."

"Swishabob."

"Yeah. Thanks fella," Dan says, gladhanding my shoulder.

They tip the bartender then walk over to socialize with the locals.

Once they're safely away, I turn to Heath and whisper, "Ur right bout doodsputtin hance on ur shouldursss..."

"Dishadoo," he confirms.

Mandy & Dan gab a few minutes with the townies. Then, true to her word, they leave. On their way out, Mandy smiles & waves at me. And I wave back.

'Who's Crying Now' queues up next on the jukebox.

I think about dragging Heath back to the Penthouse. But then the front door swings open again, and in walk Dallas & Barnes.

Needlessly, I flag them down.

"Dallas says you offered to buy us a round?" Barnes asks, plopping down in the stool next to me.

"Yeppers!"

"Everything all right with Heath?" Dallas asks.

"O. Heashfine," I answer. "Heesh bummed."

Heath raises his chin off his chest. "Bijabook," he greets Dallas & Barnes.

"Uwannanothershot?" I ask.

"Y.E.S!"

"See?" Then to the bartender: "Fore more schlots. Ananuller bugget, pleece."

FADE TO BLACK

Next morning, I wake up hungover.

And my bed's wet.

"Hello?"

Nobody answers. The Dude Room's vacant, except for me.

"Ugh. I must've blacked out."

I crawl over to my duffle bag and dig out my reserve supply of nicotine gum. Then I pop two pieces and drag myself over to the window.

I open the curtains: "Goddam!"

After my eyes adjust, I see Heath sitting out there in that lawn chair—slumped over & smoking a cigarette.

I open the window. "Morning."

"Morning," he stirs.

"I think I blacked out last night."

"Yeah... Me too."

"What's the last thing you can remember?" I ask.

"Ruining my life. You?"

"Oh right... That sucks man... I'm sorry. Dude... my shoulder's here for you and all that. But real quick: Does it smell like piss in here to you?"

"Oh yeah."

"Goddam it! I knew it. I pissed the fucking bed last night." I shake my head angrily. Then I wish I hadn't.

"Hose off your sleeping bag," Heath advises. "And your pillows and whatnot. There's some white vinegar under the sink. Mix that with warm water, then scrub all your bedding with it and let it soak for a while. Then hang everything outside on the clothesline." (Pro tip, Reader: Avoid the rental houses if you're a leaky drunk. Camp out instead. It's way easier to keep it a secret out there.)

"Thanks," I say relieved. "Sounds like you've got some experience with this."

"Fuck off."

"Hey. Before I do all that though... Dragon Punch?"

"Definitely."

(There's no better cure for a hangover in Corn than marijua-

72

na. Follow that up with a greasy breakfast & a damp morning of detasseling, and you'll be cured before noon. Especially if you're in your twenties.)

After lunch, our crew caravans back over to The Angry Day field for second pulls. Where I figure I'll share blocks, being as how I've only got a few anyway. Unfortunately, all my usual doubles partners—Heath, Wendy, Eric LeMayhew & Benji Basil—pulled twice as many blocks as me. Luckily, I soon discover that Barnes only pulled three—same as me.

Barnes & I start game planning our route over a bowl of dank ass nuggets. (You see, with second pulls being a double-rowing affair, partnering up results in you cleaning one whole block of corn (4 rows) in a single pass. So then you gotta hunt down y'all's next block on the far end of the field. And it's fucking confusing back there. The tags are torn up, covered in dirt, or missing in action. Plus, none of 'em's got your name Sharpee-ed on anyway—Just the block number, if you're lucky. There's also long stretches of bald patches &/or super-tiny corn plants. Not to mention irrigators, tire ruts, ditch weed & varmint habitats. Hence, me & Barnes mapping shit out.)

With block numbers tattooed on our forearms (under our shirtsleeves) & a backup tag with our list in my pocket, Barnes & I cash the bowl and get to work.

Pop . . . . Pop . . . . Ssss Pop.

Barnes starts yakking straight away.

"Man! You and Heath were FUCKED UP last night!" He sounds impressed.

"I know dude," I boast. "We both blacked out!"

"Ha!"

Pop . . . . Pop . . . . Ssss Pop.

"I pissed the bed."

"Yuck!"

"Haha! Just kidding."

"Good one," he says.

73

Pop . . . . *Pop* . . . . *Ssss Pop.*
"How long did we stay at the bar?" I shift gears.

"Only about a half hour after me and Dallas got there...
Guess that means you don't remember us escorting you home."

"Ha! Nope. Was I falling all over myself?"

"No, nothing like that. You kept talking shit about some
local girl. Mandy. Loud as fuck. Saying how nice she was. How
pretty. Then the jukebox cut off right as you were betting me
and Dallas you could steal her away from her boyfriend before
the season was over. It was fucking hilarious dude. Just drunk
talk. But everybody in there started eyeballing you." He starts
chuckling. "You just kept right on talking shit though. Mandy.
Mandy. Mandy. So we walked you and Heath back to the Penthouse."

"No shit?"

"Yeah."

"Thanks."

"Of course. To be fair though, we also hoped you guys'd
smoke us out."

"Did we?"

"Nope."

"Sorry."

"It's all good."

Pop . . . . *Pop* . . . . *Ssss Pop.*
"So I was mooning over Mandy huh?"

"Oh yeah. Big time."

(As you may recall Reader, due to my extreme, 2005-era
celebrity obsession, I became an infallible polygrapher of Stephen Barnes last night. Therefore, I know that everything he's
just told me about the bar last night is true. However, he's lying
about Heath & me not smoking him out—presumably because
he & Dallas are dry. So they're gonna lie & cheat & steal for
every bit of weed they can get right now. Fucking Texans: give
an inch, they'll redraw the maps.)

"So you heard anything about Sugarfield?" I change the

subject again.

"Oh yeah," Barnes titters. "He and Wendy were at the diner this morning. Get this... Sugarfield was dosing four tabs of acid (LSD) last night!"

"Holy shit! No way!"

"Yeah! Got it from those two Vermont rookies, F.Y.I. Milo and Jack. Anyways, Sugarfield says he was tripping his balls off at the bar, watching Wendy, Heath, Milo and Jack play pool. When all of a sudden he starts hallucinating on a whole 'nuther level. Says Gavin Rossdale jumped out of nowhere and tried to kill him!"

"Fucking hell!"

"Yeah! So Sugarfield runs for it right. Bolts out of there, heading for sanctuary at the Flophouse."

I start laughing.

Pop . . . . Pop . . . . Ssss Pop.

"I know I know." Barnes chokes down his own laughter. "Anyways, Sugarfield walks inside THE NEIGHBOR'S HOUSE! But he's so fucked up, he actually thinks it's the Flophouse! Told me he just figured we were out. Like that makes sense. Anyways, he lays down on this guy's living room couch because it's near the window and he wants to keep an eye out for Mr. Razorblade Suitcase."

"Bwahahaha! Nice."

"Yeah. Well 'Neighborangutan,' as you dubbed him last night—"

"—I did?"

"Yeah. Anyways, when he finally walks into the room and turns on the light, Sugarfield hares out of there like a shot. Says he thought it was Rossdale!"

I keel over & start crying.

"Oh man! That's outstanding," I finally say.

Pop . . . . Pop . . . . Ssss Pop.

"And of course... you saw the rest."

"I sure did. Goddam. Thanks for that Barnes. Hell of a

report."

"My pleasure."

Pop . . . . *Pop* . . . . *Ssss Pop.*

"Hey, did you say you saw Wendy this morning? At the diner?"

"Oh yeah, I almost forgot. Wendy chased Sugarfield down last night. Says she found him a mile up the highway, hiding behind a Bush."

"Ha! Fucking Corn."

"Fucking Corn."

Pop . . . . *Pop* . . . . *Ssss Pop.*

"Sugarfield also said Milo and Jack got plenty more acid."

"Nice." I lick my lips.

Barnes & I finish cleaning our Angry Day blocks, smoke a bowl, then I drive him back to the Flophouse. He hops out, and I head on home for a shower.

During a Corn season, shaving's right up there with hot showers. Still, I've got an itch for smooth cheeks today. So, I grab my razor and get baby-faced.

Once I'm done in the bathroom, I throw on my Sunday slacks, a collared shirt, clean sneakers & my nice pair of eyeglasses. As a final touch, I neglect my tattered field hat in exchange for Wendy's Royals baseball cap.

Then I walk outside to check my sheets.

They smell like vinegar & piss.

Time to get drunk with Barnes, I suppose.

Midway across town, I walk into a spot of Trouble. Big time. A truckful of locals seem hell bent on conscripting me into another goddam card game: Three-Card Monte.

(Now, Three-Card Monte's a game for con artists. Pure & simple, Reader. As such, you ALWAYS WANT TO BE THE DEALER. 'Cause if you're not the dealer, you're a "Mark." A.k.a. Dupe, Sucker, Chump, Patsy—you get the picture.)

Fortunately, it doesn't seem like these townies know the

score yet. They're stalking me in their truck, nipping at my heels. But they're hesitant to jump out and play.

Lucky for them, Three-Card Monte doesn't bore the shit out of me like poker does. So I turn around and wave—like I'm a gameshow host. Bob Barker here! Come on down.

Obliged, they pull up next to me.

"Hey man," the driver—who resembles a marshmallow—greets me tartly. "You're here will the detasselers right?" Next to him sit two guys that look like angry carrots.

I doff my cap & flash my Bob Barker chompers. "Yes sir. Suppose I don't look it, huh? What with these my Sunday bests on." (Three-Card Monte Pro Tip #1: playact a role. Your objective is to bamboozle your marks, Reader. So use deception & chicanery at every turn. You should even cater to your marks' prejudices, assuming you're wily enough to tease them out. For example, Cornbelt hicks like these three bedwetters typically deprecate one social bottom feeder more than all others: the Southern Rube.)

"Hey you wouldn't know where we can find a guy named JJ would ya?" the driver asks me, insinuatingly. Beady-eye-edly.

"Who?" I respond, quizzically. Brow-furrowed-ly. (Three-Card Monte Pro Tip #2: NEVER let your marks supply the cards.)

"J.J." he repeats.

"No," I explain, chuckling genially. "I mean JJ who? What's this guy's last name?"

"Oh." Realization dawns upon the marshmallow. "I don't know." He looks to his traveling companions—but they just shrug. Then he turns back to me, "Guess we didn't figure there'd be more than one."

(Classically, of the three cards getting Monte-ed Reader, it's the Ace of Spades that marks are supposed to follow. Presently, our three cards are the Campsite, the Flophouse & the Penthouse—making the latter our Ace of Spades. And though you should NEVER gamble with townies, if it becomes unavoidable like this, for the good name of all detasselers you'd better PLAY TO WIN.)

"Huh." I scratch my hairless chin. "I guess I see what you mean. Thing is, lots of these guys go by their last name. So maybe I've made his acquaintance, I just know him as Smith or Johnson or some such?" I point to my forehead all scrunch-faced & look up at the sky, as if to summon more thinkin' juice.

This last exchange effects my marks deeply. Their faces glow bright white & orange, respectively. "Maybe Sandy got his last name off a credit card," a carrot blurts. "Sandy" being the name of the human cigarette (bartender), I deduce.

(Now, I don't mind bending the rules in a card game now & again. And I consider it fair play if folks wanna throw in a wild card. But let's not forget who's dealing here.)

"You tried the campsite yet," I offer casually. "Majority of the crew's out there." I point west, down the highway. (The correct direction.)

"Thanks kid." The driver shifts into gear and races away.

"Good luck!" I smile & wave.

Their next stop's Tasseltown Taps. But that'll be a dead end—being as how I used my Mom's credit card last night. Stop number two's likely to be our campsite—assuming they can find it. But by then, Zena, Molly & Bob should be there to greet them.

Once the marshmallow & carrots are safely tucked inside the bar, I meander through a couple backyards and slip through the backdoor of the Flophouse. Then I get Barnes to run over to Casey's for me to buy some forties & a can of Copenhagen.

Epilogue #1
Legal Considerations?

Three days after the Midnight Flight of Sage Sugarfield, the "City" of Tasseltown evicts our crew from camp—despite having recommended the site. I research the cited ordinance through a Freedom of Information Request (being a second-year law student), and it turns out legit. So, during the peak of the season 80% of our crew has to move five miles farther down the highway. And though the municipality doesn't interfere with the rental houses (most likely it can't), our presence in town is greatly diminished thereafter. (Don't forget Reader: there is a huge power imbalance between a Corn crew & it's host town. And it's not in your favor.)

Epilogue #2
Romance?

I run into Mandy & Dan again, last day of the season. I'm loading all my gear into my Jeep out in front of the Penthouse, and they're just driving around. Bravely, we exchange pleasantries—as though nothing unsavory had occurred. Still, awareness permeates our chitchat like the pulp in orange juice. Failing to pierce the awkwardness with my gregarious oratory, I ludicrously, or perhaps brilliantly, invite them to our end-of-the-season crew party.

Inconceivably, they promise to stop by!

At that party, Wendy's still dating Sugarfield.

Heath's still bummed. But less so.

Sadly, neither Mandy nor Dan attends. (No doubt for the best, Reader. The culture shock they would have experienced may well have destroyed Detasseler–Townie foreign policy for a generation.)

Finally, Lillie Gillespie's star will soon shine brighter than Madonna's. Then fade. Then settle on a par with Sarah MacLauchlan.

Barnes marries a teacher.

Invocation

Doing great so far dedicated Reader. You know the job. You know the digs. You know the ethos. If thrown into a cornfield, you'd land on your feet. Just got to complete some advanced coursework and you'll be ready to graduate.

In point of fact, this next Corn Story levees the heaviest lesson I've got for you. It'll likely save your life! Like most hard learning though, you'll have to earn it with blood, sweat & tears. So I guess you'd best prepare for that, emotionally-wise. I do pray for your kind indulgence, whiplashed Reader.

As disclosed in the Preface, (other than myself) I use people's real names sparingly within this curriculum. Well, you'll find them in this next piece. My reasoning is simple. And solemn.

To honor the Dead:

Two Trees No Stop Signs

Or *Aaron's Ariadne's Thread*

*What once was will always be, no matter how long
we refuse to see.* – Aaron Robert Wilkinson

Emotionally, I've got two left brains. Always have. But ever
since my mental health breakdown ten years ago, I've been
learning emotions best I can. And let me tell you: Grief's a hot
pot of shit soup.

I'm just gonna have to stomach it though. Else I can't teach
you my heaviest lesson about corn detasseling.

*It's all right. You'll be just fine this time—
talking to yourself like a long-lost friend.* (A.R.W.)

Here goes: On July 25, 2000, Heidi Renee Richey (Hendrix
College '01) died in a car accident during Corn. She was on my
crew.

I drove up to the scene of her accident. It revisits me often—
via nightmare & my OCD brain. Reeling through my mind like
this...

FADE IN:

EXTERIOR (BIRD'S EYE). Rural Central Iowa's X-Y
axis: checkerboard plats. A few miles west of Scranton.
Gravel, paved, composite & dirt roads. Day.

EXTERIOR (ZOOM IN). Black 1998 Jeep Grand Cher-
okee. Speeding down a gravel road between two tall cornfields.

INTERIOR. Dusty, dank Jeep cabin.

ME, the driver. It's obvious, subconsciously, to ME that something's horribly wrong up the road. But ME's an emotional coward who can neither look squarely at the catastrophe, nor accept what it might imply. Still, ME's a great actor who can make such a contradiction apparent for the audience.

ROMAN (A.K.A. "RAMEN" LIKE THE NOODLES) HOLIDAY, riding shotgun.

HUCKLEBERRY COBBS, backseat—behind ME.

ALAN HICKEY (childhood friend of ME & HOLIDAY, from Conway, Arkansas), backseat—behind HOLIDAY.

                    HOLIDAY
That's not Heidi's car. (Shakes his head back and forth.)

ME parks on the roadside, several yards shy of the accident. COBBS & HICKEY rubberneck around HOLIDAY, peering out his open window.

                    ME
           This doesn't even seem real.

                                        CUT TO:
EXTERIOR (FLASH IMAGES). (Old & grainy; sepia.) Gravel intersection. No stop signs. A grocer's truck sits mid-intersection. Diagonally. Hood smashed. In the ditch opposite, a Green Metal Nightmare (wreckage—1996 Honda CR-V). Behind the intersection, in the background: a single large tree afore a sprawling beanfield.

EXTERIOR (ZOOM IN). (Vivid Color.) Green Metal Nightmare.

AARON WILKINSON, corn detasseler, musician, philosopher, Texas State high diving champion. His face (Captain Jack Sparrow come *Matrix* Twins) emerges from the far side of the wreckage.

                                              CUT TO:
INTERIOR. Jeep cabin.

                    HOLIDAY
              Holy Shit! Is that Aaron!?
                                              CUT TO:
EXTERIOR. Green Metal Nightmare.
                                              CUT TO:
INTERIOR. Jeep cabin.
                                              CUT TO:
EXTERIOR. Green Metal Nightmare.
                                              CUT TO:
INTERIOR. Jeep cabin.
                    ETC. (Continue flashing back & forth
                    until you've produced the desired evo-
                    cation of doom & disorientation.)

EXTERIOR. ZOOM OUT into a bird's eye view of the road.

WILKINSON emerges from inspecting the wreckage. After bounding up the ditch, he walks slowly, warily, along the road—toward the Jeep. (The onset of this stroll should reveal the small, intact teal Ford Ranger pickup he'd been driving—previously obscured by the grocer's truck & tall corn. The Ranger's parked under that large tree, on the far side of the intersection.) This emotionally-charged prome-

83

nade will be the establishing shot for our lead character. So get it right! WILKIINSON is surefooted and calm. But emotionally punch-drunk. Still, like a lot of things with AARON WILKINSON, punch-drunk comes off pensive & conscientious. Evoking these complex sensibilities, WILKINSON approaches the Jeep's passenger-side (HOLIDAY'S) window.

CUT TO:

INTERIOR: Jeep cabin.

WILKINSON clasps his fingers onto HOLIDAY's open window. Then he surveys the Jeep's cabin for a couple beats. (He's making sure the victim's boyfriend, GUS BANKS, is not in the back seat. As well as just being deliberate before he speaks.) Meanwhile, the four Jeep characters are anxious & unnerved.

AARON WILKINSON
She's gone... Heidi's gone.

HOLIDAY
What the FUCK!

ME, COBBS & HICKEY
What the fuck!

After a dissonant medley of "What the fuck," a few beats pass in silent paroxysm. Ultimately, the camera focuses in on WILKINSON, as he emotes a momentary mental & emotional absence. After which, he springs back into the present moment: like his Soul just woke up from a nap. This back-to-reality moment is palpable: prompting (cueing) the other characters to respond.

COBBS
Is there something we can do?

ME
I don't know. I'm not very good with this kind of shit.
(ME incorrectly assumes COBBS is speaking to him—rather
than to WILKINSON.)

HICKEY
We could go for help?

ME
I've got my cell phone.
(Same.)

AARON WILKINSON
The other driver got a ride with a local.
Said the EMTs were on their way, from Carroll,
but he didn't want them getting lost.

COBBS
What happened?

AARON WILKINSON
I didn't see it... must've got here right after...
But, neither one of them stopped.

FADE OUT.

*So I was chatting with that bird sitting at my window
about my plans to fly away.*

*He said, "my friend, I know that song you're singing—
'cause if I had your legs I'd run
so far away." (A.R.W.)*

In real life, the above SCENE elapsed no more than two or three minutes. Holiday & I, more so than Cobbs & Hickey, damn near scarpered through the floorboard, Flintstone-car-style, trying to get away. Aaron said to us: "It's fine, guys. Go on ahead to that field. Seriously: Here are my block numbers." But I've relived that whole incident for a couple decades now, and I'm positive he wanted us to stay. Aaron was just too classy, too magnanimous, to burden us by saying so.

Blind to such realities then, I drove away.

Leaving Aaron to pace that road alone.

Pain regrets. And wisdom forgets. (A.R.W.)

It's four-way intersections everywhere you drive in rural Iowa, disappointed-in-me Reader. And hundreds, possibly thousands don't have any stop signs. One of the reasons for this is that visibility remains unobstructed from Fall until Spring: as the corn's still short, the beans never grow above your shins, and Iowa's flatter than its own maps. Furthermore, even in July, only about half the cornfields will block your view (for reasons too numerous to mention). So, you can't blame the citizenry, nor their local governments, for Heidi's accident. Similarly, you can't blame yourself. Even if you, personally, sped through every blind intersection you came to that year (and the year before). You're not responsible. Indeed, such blame-seeking points of view are called "cognitive distortions." And they spring from Grief-avoidance. In reality, Grief's just real fucking heavy. And it'll pollute your mind unless you learn how to deal with it.

Despite attending the same college, I barely knew Heidi Richey before that summer. I did know her boyfriend though: Gus Banks. Gus & I worked on the same crew (Scranton) the previous summer. He drove an old Volkswagen Bus (the ultimate hippie chariot), which he kept parked at the campsite for everyone's use. We Arkansans, especially at mealtimes, tended to hub there—as Gus was from Clinton. The addition of Heidi in 2000 improved our mess hall vibe into a family bistro-like atmosphere. Such is how I came to know her: breaking bread at Scranton Camp. Heidi was warm, intelligent & kind.

And her accident tore our crew's heart out. None more so than Gus. But Aaron Wilkinson was a close second. Not to be a gossip, but there'd been a bit of a love triangle swirling around camp. I never learned any details (intentionally), but I certainly watched Gus transform into a red-faced, shaking-mad lunatic for a couple days whenever Aaron came around. Bravely, our short, wiry crew boss Tom Pater facilitated a reconciliation between these two silverbacks a week prior to Heidi's accident.

After which, Gus & Aaron grieved together like brothers. Arm in arm. For three days.

Morning of July 29th, we held a service for Heidi at Scranton Camp—out in the beanfield.

Then, we all drove "home."

When Hendrix College resumed in the Fall, Tom and his business partners Bob & Mona Sturgis planted a memorial tree for Heidi on campus. A Cucumber Magnolia, or "Cucumber Tree": *Magnolia acuminata*. Almost immediately, I found myself talking to it. Often. And I wasn't alone. As evidence, I'd find little porcelain & plastic critters—squirrels, chipmunks, foxes, rabbits, birds, dogs & cats, etc.—assembled round the trunk. Sometimes, these animals would band together atop the mounted plaque, as if on stage, but careful not to obscure the quote: "EVERWHERE YOU SING YOUR SMILE."

It's good for me to see that the sun—ashining—
is the only thing that's standing in my way. (A.R.W.)

Three years later, on June 29th, 2003, Aaron Wilkinson died in New York City. Ordinarily, he and I both would've already been in Missouri (MO) Valley, Iowa, working on Bob Sturgis's early rogueing crew. But the corn was running late that year.

By the time I did get to MO Valley, Aaron's news had already spread & we all felt raw as hell. It shrouded that whole season. Case in point: I don't remember much. Sure, I was drinking (excessively) and smoking weed (amply), but that's no different from the other summers. And I remember all five of those. But the only clear memory I've retained from '03 is me lounging on my Jeep's hood, blaring Aaron's music into a cornfield.

"Heroin overdose" spread with the news of his death. Like a shadow. Admittedly, our Society's made some progress since then. But back in 2003, heroin overdose meant "Junkie." Big time. Even amongst us migrant-farming hippies. Problem was, "Junkie" just didn't fit with the Aaron Wilkinson we all knew. Junkies were supposed to be skuzzy, scheming sad sacks. Meanwhile, Aaron loved life—with ferocity. He loved other people. And aside from that aforementioned moment of magnanimity at the site of Heidi's accident (telling us he was fine with us leaving), Aaron was honest, forthright & as real as they come. Even nice about it (mostly). Aaron dying a junkie's death just didn't make any sense.

Over the years, I've assembled the following facts:

Aaron graduated from Hendrix in May of 1999. After which, he worked at a liquor store & knocked around Central Arkansas until he left for Corn. Following that '99 detasseling season, Aaron hitched a ride over to New York City and found an apartment. There he wrote songs, made friends & familiarized himself with the music scene on the Lower East Side (of Manhattan). Come late June of 2000, he carpooled back to Iowa with some New York Corn folk. After our '00 season ended tragically, Aaron roamed the Country for a couple months. Honestly, he was probably drinking a lot of whiskey. Then around mid-September, he turned up in Wisconsin for apple-picking season. (Five to six weeks of climbing ladders, filling up buckets & emptying those buckets into giant bins.) After Apples, he thumbed it back to New York.

And for the next three years, Aaron repeated the same pattern I've just outlined. So, it's pretty impressive that he became something of a Rock Star's rock star around The City. Just four successive spells of eight months: Plenty of time, apparently, to reignite NYC's Anti-Folk music scene. Aaron was a rising tide: steady gigs, recording, touring. He was hanging out with Regina Spektor, The Moldy Peaches & The Strokes!

And then he was gone.

*When you think that you've got everything
that Winter Wind's at your door.* (A.R.W.)

So that godawful Green Metal Nightmare? I started dreaming it, occasionally, after Heidi Richey's death. But Aaron dying kicked it into overdrive. Somehow his & Heidi's deaths got all twisted up in my subconscious, and stuck that way. Even started harassing me while I was awake, thanks to my ever-sharpening OCD brain. Admittedly, the long passage of time (20 years) has tamped it down. Considerably. But it's still there. Eliciting some miserable thoughts over the years. Like: did Aaron get too close to Death in that ditch—to his detriment? Is Death contagious like that? Did I doom Aaron by not sharing in the burden? More specifically, had I commiserated with him at the site of Heidi's accident, would Aaron be alive today? Conversely, would that have resulted in my own death? Or Holiday's, Cobbs's or Hickey's? Also, what about the Dead? Is my Green Metal Nightmare preventing Aaron & Heidi from their eternal rests? Did I steal their Souls like some devil? Or inherit guardian angels?

Just breath to hold. (A.R.W.)

Aaron's family planted a memorial tree at Hendrix too. A Red Maple: *Acer rubrum*. It stands on the opposite side of the Mills Center from Heidi's Cucumber Magnolia. Though perhaps I should say it "towers," as it's grown 30 feet.

Meanwhile, Heidi's Tree has struggled. Magnolias *can* fatten up like whales. Especially around Conway. But Heidi's Tree got planted too close to a copse of oaks & pines. In combination, these older trees & the long roof of the Mills Center block out the sun too much. Still, Heidi's Tree does look healthy—if runt-ish. Her roots must've plunged a good long way over the years.

Most people don't know this, but trees have their own Underworlds. Seriously—I'm not just being metaphorical. (Though of course I am). Quite literally, trees plug their roots into a vast underground network of fungi. A "Woods Wide Web." When not being punny, Biologists call these fungal labyrinths "mychorrhizal networks." And here's how they work: The mychorrhizal fungi serves as a telecommunication & nutri-ent-delivery system for every tree & plant that "subscribes" to its sprawling infrastructure of buried fiber-optic cables (myce-lium). In exchange for network access, these client-plants "pay" the fungi with sugary carbohydrates. The more sweet carbs a plant feeds into the mychorrhizal network, the more assistance/access provided to that plant's roots. To illustrate: Let's say a bug scourge erupts among a forest's hickories. The affected trees will wire an S.O.S. into their network. The unaffected trees & other "online" plants will then relay whatever aid & armaments they can spare, via fungus. Additionally, the mychorrhizal fungi, itself, may provide limited assistance—especially for its best sug-ar-suppliers. Thusly, the forest, collectively, wages its bug war: the health & safety of its surface-dwelling constituents depen-dent upon the quality & quantity of its underworld ties.

It's almost a guarantee that Heidi's Cucumber Tree has plugged its roots into the mychorrhizal network beneath Hen-drix's campus. The whole town of Conway's rich with the stuff. For millennia, we were a tallgrass prairie. Toadstools pop up ev-erywhere. But the best evidence that Heidi's roots have reached the network is that her Tree's still standing, if barely over my head. We've had some scorching hot summers lately. And most of the other saplings around Campus have died.

I'm actually standing in front of her Tree right now. Literally. It's Spring, and Heidi's flowers are blooming: Eggshell and Buttermilk. I came here to drop off a funny ceramic bird I found. (He's smoking a corncob pipe!) When I'm done, I'll walk over to Aaron's Tree. Some days though, I visit Aaron's Tree first. Just depends on how I'm feeling. And, honestly, where I park. Either way, I'm always listening to Aaron's music on my iPod. Same tunes I was blasting into that '03 cornfield.

Like usual, I get to wondering how Aaron dealt with Heidi's death. I mean, he saw the Green Metal Nightmare first. And dove right in! You don't just brush off that level of trauma, right?

But I never brought it up.

Then, Aaron was gone.

So now I talk to trees.

Still, I suspect he handled it the same way then, as his Red Maple Tree does now: roots connected to Heidi's beneath the surface; allies in an underworld of healthy, albeit transactional, give-and-take.

But where does that leave you & me, Dear Reader? Sure, unless you're crazier than I ever was, you've learned to STOP AT THE FUCKING INTERSECTIONS in Corn. Such ends my heaviest Corn lesson, by the way. But literarily-wise, doesn't it feel like we've been left in the lurch? Where's our satisfying conclusion? The big payoff? Besides, I woke up just last night sweating from my Nightmare again.

So, no. We're not done yet.

Would I were a Tree. Then I could just plug my roots into the underground fungi here at Hendrix Campus and speak directly to my friends. First, I'd tell Heidi, "I'm sorry I didn't stop at the stop signs. You were a rookie, and I should have provided you with a better example." Then, I'd ask Aaron: "You must've had the Green Metal Nightmare too, right? How did you cope with it?"

Sadly, my roots remain metaphorical. (At best.)

So let's get literal again. Shall we? Worked last time. All that nerdy mychorrizal network stuff might not have explained *how* Aaron coped, but it gave us a useful description of the end result.

You got any ideas, Reader? How we might, literally, attain Aaron's point of view on Heidi's memory?

If you answered, "Climb his Red Maple Tree to look out over that building and onto Heidi's Cucumber Tree," then you and I may share a mychorrizal network of our own.

Hell, nobody's around. Let me just make my way around the Mills Center...

"Hello, Aaron's Tree."

And I'm up. These bottom branches are super thick. Pretty dense, too—They keep slapping me. A big one just poked my leg & restarted my iPod through my jeans.

I climb ten feet. Fifteen. And it's slap, slap, slap, poke, poke, poke, the whole way up.

At twenty feet, I start getting frustrated: "Stop poking my iPod Aaron's Tree!"

At twenty-five feet, the foliage finally thins out. But now my problem's toeholds. Can't see over the Mills Center's roof just yet. And every step up looks risky as fuck. "Oooh... shit," this is one bendy-ass branch! One more might do it though. Do I risk it?

No weight rests upon these shoulders
that could cause my back to break. (A.R.W.)

We all deal with Grief in our own ways. Some of us don't deal with it at all. Opting instead to run away. For years. Swapping real life out for a movie scene—so we can leave the theater if we don't like the show. But running away only works for so long. Always, the show must go on.

Fortunately, like trees, we humans have subterranean networks. We just have to learn, individually, how to access them. For me, the answer is poetry. For others: family, religion, meditation, service, sports, Nature, etc. But whatever does it for *you*, Dear Reader, I recommend figuring it before you're out-of-shape ass gets caught swaying 30 feet up in a tree! Branches slapping the hell out of you. Restarting the same song on your iPod over and over and...

—oh my God!

Mercury and Diamonds!
The stars came aflashing! (A.R.W.)

Holy Shit, Aaron! You sly Texas troubadour! You almost made me fall out of your Tree just now. Good thing it's as dense as me... I can't believe I'm just now figuring this out. You just changed her name! Oh shit, here come the tears. I appreciate the view Sir. Heidi's Tree looks great from up here. But I'd better climb down, or I might not make it.

On the way down, Aaron's branches neither slap nor poke me. Not once.

When I touch down, my foot serendipitously underscores the quote on his plaque.

"I'M NOT AS FAR AWAY AS YOU THINK." it reads.

Back on solid ground, Reader. Now let me just unplug my headphones and play this song through my speaker for you. You need to hear this:

Fair Margret – Aaron Robert Wilkinson

Now I rolled out to see fair Margret down below the willow's shade
And her fallen hair in a silent slumber gently on her chest it lay
And her breast did heave and draw a shadow
upon the grass it likewise swayed

And with no song my voice I swallowed and with a sigh
    my tongue I betrayed
For how could I mock pride and valor and vainly stand
    in chivalry's shame
And wake the eyes of sleeping Margret and beg her join
    my selfish game?

But in a moment's calm and as still as daylight—
an artist's hunger and a poet's dream
I suffered all of her joy and her sorrow
as summer... as autumn... as winter... as spring...

Enough mercury and diamonds, the stars came a-flashing
and the taste of the air was again my own
I stood among the thorns and the rocks of the valley
with no chance but for the dawn, and no choice but forward to go

So turn me now ye saints of the traveled
and guide me true on my wondering way
I hear the voices sing soft as rain and sure as thunder
that the promise of tomorrow is forsaken by today

Visual Aids

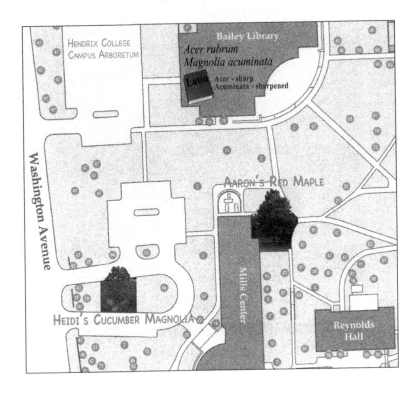

All of the italicized, centered quotes
in "Two Trees No Stop Signs" are song lyrics from:

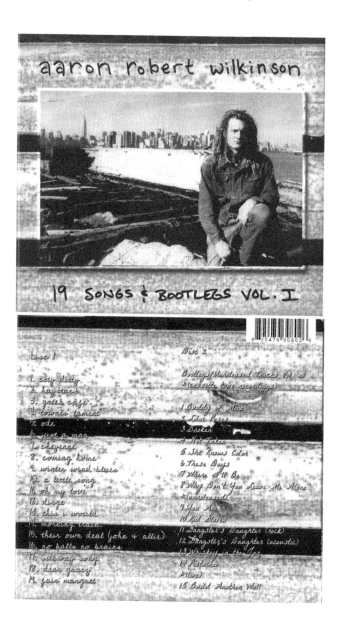

September 10, 2003
http://www.ericrosenfield.com/blog/archives/000130.html
Aaron Wilkinson

Two days ago I was at the Sidewalk bar with my friend Jon, and, on a thought, I turned to him and asked if he'd seen Aaron around.

"He's dead." Said Jon. I asked him if he was serious.

I guess Aaron wasn't the closest friend of mine; he was just a guy I used to hang out with every once and a while. We played music together a couple times but mostly we'd talk about books. He had white-boy dreadlocks down his back and an easy southern accent and undoubtedly it's my own prejudices at work that, looking at him, I would never have expected him to be as sharp a guy as he was. But he was sharp as hell and had excellent taste in books and a degree in philosophy. I leant him a Philip Roth book once; it took him a year to get around to reading it, and then one time I bumped into him and he peeked the book out of the bag and went "Look what I'm reading. It's really great.", and then he finished it very quickly. He was a gigging musician and song-writer, and a good one and the last couple times I saw him he told me he was working on some fiction. He had read some of my writing, and he wanted me to look over the piece he was working on when he had finished it.

The last time I saw him we were sitting at the Sidewalk talking about the Argentinian writer Jorge Louis Borges. I had heard of Borges, heard he was fantastic, but though I hadn't read him in talking with Aaron I pretended I had because I wanted to seem cool or something. I have an unhealthy tendency towards that kind of thing, pretending I know things I don't actually know to keep this image I have in my mind of being a, well, a know-it-all. That was in April or so, and June 1st I went away to Europe, bringing three Borges books with me. Coming back I was looking forward to having a _real_ conversation with Aaron on the subject, to actually be able to engage in a literary discussion about this writer who writes in a way that makes you feel lost when you look up from his book, confused that reality seems less tangible than the world of his prose.

I wasn't around to see Aaron's deterioration. I wasn't around when my friend James hadn't heard from him in so long that he broke into Aaron's apartment to find Aaron five days cold with a needle in his arm. I found James later that night, he starts shaking as he tells me about it.

And the thing about it is that I've known heroin addicts before - guys with bulging eyes who are constantly hitting you up for money and have trouble stringing one sentence coherently after the next. Aaron wasn't anything like that - this was a guy who could

97

talk at length about Sartre and Kant. And I guess part of the reason his death bothers me so much is because in my own mind people who are smart and educated and likable and talented aren't supposed to become smack heads. It doesn't fit in with my picture of the world.

Aaron's not supposed to be dead.

I don't know, I wasn't there for the memorial they had for him in July, I just found out about this thing that people around here have been coping with already for two months. So I guess I just wanted to tell somebody what I was feeling. So I'm telling all of you. He was my friend and now he's dead and I find the whole thing kind of baffling and confusing and depressing.

Aaron Robert Wilkinson
1976-2003
RIP

Posted by Eric Rosenfield at September 10, 2003 07:21 PM | Comments

thanks for posting this message. i was a philosophy major at hendrix college with aaron and had similar experience with him as you. jamie

Posted by: jamie evans on October 21, 2003 10:08 PM

Well... I'm embarrassed to admit I'd never heard of Aaron Wilkinson before (especially since I, like you, am one of those assholes who can't afford to admit I didn't know a "cool-bohemian-arty" fact, writer, record, person... you name it.) In fact: I didn't get to your site out of nothing but a really-really shallow reason: I'm reviewing Room On Fire, which is dedicated to Wilkinson's memory... The Strokes, whose greatness endanger really cool well-kept secrets, got me here... Well, fuck that... I just wanted to tell you, don't really know why, that I got a hold of his work doing research for my review and thought it was amazing... And I think that's really cool, considering I'm just some struggling writer from Venezuela (pardon my english, btw)... So, just in case Wilkinson's image suddenly blows out of proportion due to the overexposure of being the subject of a dedicatory in perhaps the greatest rock record in a decade, remember this message... It may be bad and you may run into some asswipes that will bear his face in some 20$ tee-shirts, but at least artists and curious idiots from all around the world will actually get to appreciate what he did while being alive...

3pF

ps.- sorry bout my english... im kinda hungover, but I know if I did't write it now I would forget to do so later...

Posted by: César Elster on October 27, 2003 02:08 AM

Our family just found this site and have read the remarks by Eric and Cesar. To Eric, thank you for your affirmations of this amazing young man. He was very bright, a marvelous poet but, most of all, he was someone who loved and accepted others, always seeking to encourage their own abilities or, at least, to brighten their day with kindness. Oh, he was real, to be sure, as our family can attest. But his heart was shaped by love and he was passionate about life.
To Cesar, you might be interested to know that The Strokes have been most gracious and kind to our family since Aaron died. We met Julian and Fabrizio at the memorial gathering which Lach organized at the Sidewalk Cafe in New York in July. We've stayed in touch with them through Juliet in their management office and she and Julian called us when the new album was finished to tell us about the dedication. The on November 7th, the day before Aaron's 27th birthday, we went to their concert in Houston and they received us like honored guests in their dressing rooms before and after the show. Their new album is great, to be sure, but their kindness to the parents of a friend has been exceptional.
I'd like to post more to this site in the days ahead to tell you some stories about how Aaron touched peoples' lives. We find comfort in those remembrances to help us deal with the questions and heartache from his death.
Watch for a website by another of his friends in the city, Hogan Long. He's waiting on us to get some of Aaron's music to him. Despite my fatherly prejudice, Aaron really was an amazing songwriter.

Dennis -- the dad

Posted by: Dennis Wilkinson on November 22, 2003 12:55 PM

hey.........
aaron was my older brother. i was away in micronesia teaching as a volunteer the last year he was alive. it is beautiful, sad, unreal and so special to find comments and stories about him.
eric, you are completely right on with the decree that aaron wasnt a junkie. he lived his life in such a way that made, and continues to do so, people admire his raw and uncensored attack on life. he embraced the joy and pain, the light and dark,.....he wrote with the pen of a true philosopher and the sweetness of a poet of life.
i am back in texas and all day he's still with me. he isnt here, though.
i havent yet fully expressed this yet, but that is the way ...ccrrr...this is the way he did

things. he always has and obviously still does keep people intrigued and on the edge of curiosity. what is it about this guy that some writer in brooklyn feels compelled to post this note? why did the strokes dedicate their album to him? why are we all still coping with the reality of the situation?
because he was beautiful.
he also was my older brother and kicked the hell out of me while i was growing up. but my family and i move from uncontrollable laughter bringing up stories about aaron throwing a cheesebuger against the wall on xmas eve when in high school and then to a river of tears from the grief cause the fifth piece of our whole isnt around to hug, kiss, smell, (mmmm he always had a some kind of smell...his dreds, guinness habbit..) but up and off he did go, leaving us here all alone. things are still ticking on. i have all of his songbooks, journals, bootlegs, master copies of recordings, future tatoo sketches, ...if anyone wants some of his music or is interested in pictures or anything....just get in touch with me. gramwilkie@hotmail.com

"oh and these days, i find myself thinkin' on and on and on...that this ol' world will just'a keep on tickin' long, long, long, long, long...after i'm gone." – aaron robert wilkinson

we're still here. he'd be pissed if we didnt do the only thing we are supposed to do while here ....
.......LIVE.

Posted by: graham wilkinson on November 22, 2003 12:56 PM

He once told me we were like trains--we each had our own courses to take, but he assured me we'd cross paths again later. and we will. Aaron has a deep soul. mmm.

Posted by: Meg C. on December 21, 2003 08:45 PM

I just want to say that I have been a struggling musician for say 17 years i am 35 now,i am embarrased to say before the strokes room on fire came out that i did not know of aaron wilkison and i am sad that i will never get to know him , but just by researching on the internet for the dedication of their cd i found his poetry , his music and a beautiful voice,i know when somebody has feeling and he sure has i am a fan for life now so all i want to say is thank you

Posted by: philip sbailo on January 2, 2004 03:25 PM

I did'nt really know Aaron personally, but I grew up in Wichita Falls, where his

100

family lives now. The one thing I will always remember about Aaron was his Thelonious Monk t-shirt. I don't know why it intrigued me so much, but I went out and bought a Monk cd because of it. He sparked my love for jazz through an insignificant t-shirt.

Posted by: Tim Handrick on February 11, 2004 08:24 PM

February 20, 2004 --So, I'm listening to Bob Dylan on my headphones on the subway and I'm being all isolated and internal and unmindful -- tired and poor and irritated so I'm trying not to recognize people as people cuz it's easier not to, sometimes.. and then the opening chords of "Most of the Time" come on, and the train surfaces on the bridge and the sun is hitting the water and bouncing back and Brooklyn is gleaming up at me and all of a sudden I'm crying about Aaron, seven months later and out of the blue I'm crying my damn eyes out. And I guess I should be embarrassed but I'm not. I miss him. It was a different city, knowing he was in it, this face from home. I remember one night right after he had gotten back from apples or corn, and I was talking to a mutual friend from college on the phone outside Lucy's on 8th and A, and Aaron wandered up drunk and I was delighted, so happy, and I stood on a crate and we pressed foreheads together to keep our balance as we both shouted at Hugh on the cellphone, and it was the first time I'd ever run into a friend on the street HERE, in this enormous place.And that was what I thought of on the train, and so I tried to see all these people sitting as strangers next to me as PEOPLE, you know, with favorite jokes and lost loves and regrets. Like he did, or always tried to do. And they looked back (of course, I WAS bawling, maybe that's why)and seemed to see me too. And I thanked him, even though I'm not sure if I think he can hear...I thanked him.
I miss Graham,too, and he's just in Texas. If you see him, or talk to him, tell him there's kids up here in NYC who think about him all the time.

Posted by: smashlie on February 20, 2004 09:43 PM

I met Aaron in Austria and he was always so gentle and really beautiful. I will always remember his smile!

Posted by: maja on February 29, 2004 06:59 PM

that's my big brother.
that's my best friend.

i know some of you remember him... i know a lot of you miss him... but i love him more than you know.

my hands are wet from wiping tears, and it's already march. most people think i'm doing better. one question - how can you EVER be better after missing someone like aaron?? it seems you don't heal. i don't want to heal. i miss him too bad. real bad.

"sometimes i take your picture and i turn it to the wall, because you are still a cliff and baby i still know how to fall..." kris

sarah lu

Posted by: sarah lu on March 23, 2004 10:43 PM

oh man...i met aaron in 1999 doing corn detasseling in iowa and he and everybody else i met there were/are family. 3 years in those fields and the last time aaron, james and i drove my truck from baltimore to iowa together. i remember him jumping a fence probably somewhere in nebraska just to walk in the corn and make that first connection with it. aaron wasn't a friend that i saw all the time.in fact the only time i was physically around him were those weeks camping and walking through corn, but i'll never ever be without him now. there's something so intense in that experience of all those people working/living together and really taking care of one another. i talked to aaron on the phone maybe a month before he died. i miss his voice a lot, the southern drawl (i'm from texas too)and i remember the charming way he'd call me darlin'. we were talking about whether either one of were going to do corn that summer. how being in grimy cities got us down and spending time out in those fields and the sun gave us back vitality and perspective. but he seemed like he was doing well and he had lots of good stuff going on. so we said goodbye and i didn't go to do corn for many reasons and then about mid-july i checked my email and found out about his death. too late for the memorial. it was hard being in a city where nobody else knew him but my boyfriend james. we spilled some whiskey for him and listened to his cd and after it had played once it quit working and has refused to play since. i really need a new copy. so life moves on, but it keeps catching me at strange moments that that short time was my time allotted to spend with such an amazing person. and it really makes me miss and savor all the other people that have moved through my life. thank you aaron.

april

Posted by: april wood on March 25, 2004 11:32 PM

...

Hydration Station

I don't know about you Reader, but I just leaked a bunch of water out of my eyes. Which reminds me: you can absolutely screw around and give yourself a heat stroke while detasseling corn. So, how 'bout I teach you how to not do that? Then, we can resume the lighthearted romps. Deal?

Good.

Sadly, not everyone's fortunate enough to grow up in Arkansas—where our humidity bidets your ass crack all summer long. Thus, most people will find Iowa Julys mighty sweltering. But no matter how high your butt sweat climbs, you'll want to drink lots of WATER WATER WATER. Such advice may seem too self-evident to mention, but you'd be surprised. Most detasselers are aged eighteen to twenty-five. In six summers, I carried three of these "young adults" out of the fields.

But that's not going to be you, is it?

The earliest warning sign of heat exhaustion—for a detasseler—is dehydration. More alarm bells would be nice. But fatigue, soreness & sweat are all just tools of the detasseling trade. Making dehydration the first manifestation that detasselers notice. Problem is, dehydration's a lot like a tornado siren: If you're aware of it, then a SPIRALING VORTEX OF DOOM is already fast approaching.

Thankfully, dehydration *does* elicit clear early warning signs. The first of these is dry mouth. But detasselers rarely notice it, because we're all potheads with cottonmouth. Thus, it's the second sign of dehydration that detasselers usually heed: a funky change in urine color. If your pee starts trickling out looking like Sunkist cola or Mountain Dew, you're dehydrated. The third sign of dehydration is a reduction—leading to the cessation—of sweat. This is when shit's getting dangerous. If you don't stop to rest & drink lots of WATER WATER WATER right now, you're being an asshole. The fourth sign of dehydration, called the "Prickly Heats," usually comes simultaneous with the sweat reduction. Also called Tinglies, Dry Itchies & Electric Rash, it'll feel like you're getting swarmed with (phantom) needle pricks. Might feel it all over your body, might be localized to your face or elsewhere. Lastly, the fifth sign of dehydration is when little red bumps start popping up. This is called a heat rash (Miliaria).

But that's not going to be you, is it?

Here's a good, unambiguous rule to follow: if you're no longer sweating, STOP WORKING IMMEDIATELY. You have taxed your body to the limit. If you don't stop right now, you could die. Seriously. Sure, it's way more likely you'll just pass out. But still, you really want to risk dying over some corn? Plus, you're in for a world of hurt anyways. You ever see those medical pictures of tetanus patients all pretzeled-up? Well that's going to be you, just as soon as you stop moving. Go ahead and clear a wide berth in the dirt. Yeah yeah... I know: you're invincible right? Ha! And do try to remember—while you're spasming & writhing around in pain down there—that you're actually getting off easy. You could've gone into shock.

But that's not going to be you, right?

So, your sweating's all fucked up, huh? Well, sit down hot-shot. Pop a squat under those tall-ass, shady corn plants. Drink lots of WATER WATER WATER. Give it a few, then see how you feel.

Still feeling bad? Not to worry. We'll get you fixed up. If you're able, head on over to your crew boss's truck—and make sure to snatch your water jug along the way. (Send a buddy if you're still cooling off.) The truck's parked at the front end of the field. You see that 5-gallon cooler of ice-cold water sitting on the tailgate? Well, behind it you'll find twenty to thirty rogueing shovels splayed about the bed like a snakes' den. Under that heap of shovels, somewhere, lies the first aid kit. It looks like an elementary school pencil box. Found it? Good. Now open it up. You're looking for two things: Emergen-C packets (like tea bags) & magnesium effervescent tablets (in a small bottle).

Now, open two of those Emergen-C packets and dump the contents into your water jug. Next, fill your jug with cold water from the tailgate cooler, close the lid, shake it up and take a few swigs. After that, put a couple/three magnesium tablets on your tongue and let those dissolve. Then wash 'em down with the rest of your Emergen-C cocktail.

Now walk around. Stay loose. Play hacky sack. Stretch. You can eat a banana and/or drink pickle juice if you want to, but it's a little late in the game for potassium to fix this. After five or ten minutes of relaxed, light movement, sit down. Be still for a while. If you don't start cramping up, you should be good to go! Of course, now all the early warning signs of dehydration we previously discussed should be ameliorated as well.

It's important to note though: I AM NO PHYSICIAN. I just did this to my own body a lot.

One last tip for managing dehydration while detasseling: EAT EAT EAT. Breakfast. Lunch. Dinner. Snacks throughout the day. EAT. Because detasseling involves so much walking, a nutrition deficit can cramp you up as bad as insufficient hydration. By way of reference, long-trail hikers will know what I'm talking about.

One final, final note: WEAR SUNSCREEN. I've heard 30 SPF's all you need, but 50's bound to be better, right? One year, I wore 100 SPF—Didn't even get a tan. Anyways, I've got no idea how SPF works. Nor how sunscreen interacts with heat exhaustion and dehydration. But I figured this tidbit fit better here than elsewhere.

Early Rogueing Crew

Can't write the book on Corn without it focusing heavily on detasseling—That's just the nature of the beast. However, each & every Corn season (for our purposes) actually begins with a totally different job. One in which swiftly-roving, shovel-wielding assassins sweep the detasseling fields free of mutants.

As I disclosed in "Horsepower," seed corn is a GENETICALLY MODIFIED ORGANISM. Better known by the acronym: "GMO." Now, there's been hullaballoos & brouhahas about GMOs since long before my rookie year (1999). Conversely, or perhaps similarly, there's been hot diggity dogs & whoopees too. So, I guess you either make your peace with 'em or you don't? Either way, you love dogs right? (While dog breeds, *Canis familiaris*, might not fit today's definition of GMOs, requiring laboratory genomic engineering, I believe they make an illuminating precursor for conceptualizing the topic. Rather than genetically modified, dog breeds are considered "selectively bred." Also, I'm foreshadowing.)

Now, back to Rogueing. Imagine you're an Iowa commercial farmer. Been tending your fields for decades. So, you're bound to notice as your crops become increasingly resistant to drought & disease. Meanwhile, Farmer Nextdoor's corn tolerates pesticides as yeomanly as the Missouri River. Talking shop one morning at the local diner, You & Farmer Nextdoor decide, ingenuously, to combine your strengths: by cross-pollinating your corn crops.

Well, that's the beginnings of the Seed Corn Industry. In a nutshell.

What does all this have to do with shovel-wielding assassins? Read on.

Let's probe our hypothetical a bit further. You & Farmer Nextdoor ain't rubes, obviously. So y'all form a business entity for the new endeavor—so as to protect your other financial interests. Lawyers, Banks, Insurance Companies & Government Regulations drive both of you up the wall for months. Until finally, Spring arrives. And You & Farmer Nextdoor get to work... on behalf of newly incorporated "SeedCo," legally speaking.

Now, You & Farmer Nextdoor don't want nothing out of SeedCo except a flashy new superstrain of disease & drought resistant, plus pesticide tolerant seed corn. You'll feed whatever ears you produce to your hogs—that's all nickels and dimes. But if SeedCo successfully develops a superstrain, you two'll get rich selling it to all the other farmers.

But you've got a huge problem: neither one of you's ever GMO-ed before.

Consequently, You & Farmer Nextdoor ring up Cornbelt A&M to speak with some scientists.

Luckily, the Head Corn Professor takes your call. And explains, "Imagine, hanging on a wall perhaps, a framed picture of a cornfield. Well, essentially, a 'detasseling field'—what I propose you should create to cross-pollinate your two strains—is the picture and the frame. Several rows of male plants, the frame, protect the real prize—the hybridizing field—from foreign pollen. Like castle walls... if you'll excuse the mixed metaphor."

"Okay," Farmer Nextdoor says. "So what's a 'hybridizing field'?"

"Ah yes, it's most ingenious," the Professor coos. "One row of male plants: your strain perhaps. Followed by four rows of female plants: Farmer Nextdoor's strain (meaning You). One row of males. Four females. One male. Four females. Et cetera. *Ad nauseum*. Once the plants are ready—as the pollen will dictate—you'll detassel every female in the field, to ensure that none self-pollinate. Thereby successfully crossbreeding your two corn strains without interference."

"Hot damn," Farmer Nextdoor whistles. "Am I glad we called you!"

"Happy to help," the Professor replies. "Now, just bring me

those seeds so I can run a few tests and hone them for you."

"Er... What?" You ask.

"No big deal. Just a minor nip and tuck in my laboratory before you plant them. Nothing to worry about."

"Right... Well, you're the Scientist." You ring off, leery you may have accidently funded Cornbelt A&M for years to come.

You & Farmer Nextdoor follow the Professor's instructions to the letter. But let's face it. A cornfield's nothing like a laboratory. Mother Nature's a real mad scientist. Sure enough, as soon as the sprouts poke up, You & Farmer Nextdoor gotta call up Cornbelt A&M again.

"What's with these funky-looking plants we're getting?" You ask the Professor. "All gangly and freakshow looking."

"Ah...," the Professor chuckles. "I believe what you're describing are Chromosomal Abnormalities."

"Chromosomal Abnormalities?" You ask, a bit salty from that chuckle.

"Yes. Mutants."

"Weren't no mutants in that cornfield picture," Farmer Nextdoor interjects. "What the hell'd you do to our corn?"

"Please Sirs, it's nothing to worry about," the Professor elucidates, far more soberly. "Not every corn plant will be genetically sound. Depending upon your acreage, Chromosomal Abnormalities could, and perhaps should, occur by the thousands. Statistically, infinitesimal. But still a blight no doubt."

"Of course!" You say, realization dawning. "I should've known... been doing this long enough. We call 'em Rogues."

"Rogues?" the Professor echoes.

"Yessir. We weren't sure right off cause these detasseling fields are so new to us."

"Aha. Of course," the Professor says. "You know. Now that you mention them... I'd advise that you prevent these mutants from pollinating. With extreme prejudice. Males and Females both."

"Roger that, Professor. You got any recommendations?"

"Yes. I'd wait until the plants grow tall enough. Then hire college students and hippies to trot through the fields with shovels, severing each Chroma—... er, rogue... at the base of its stalk."

"Hmm," You mull it over. "That just might work."

"It'd better," Farmer Nextdoor mumbles.

Okay Reader, we've sufficiently explored our hypothetical to reveal the connection between Rogueing & Detasseling. Similarly, we've laid the foundation to set you loose with a rogueing shovel, should the need arise. 'Cause let's face it: *You* are not the green-thumbed Midas from our hypothetical. You are someone presently learning how to become a fieldhand.

But despite the long road to get here, there's really no need to fine-tune the concept. A Corn Story would just waste our time here. Rogueing's literally so easy a dog can do it.

As a human, however, here's what you're looking for:

You can spot a rogue corn plant best at its brace roots. Brace roots encircle the stalk near the ground & claw into the dirt. They're a convenient bullseye because you'll fell the stalk directly above them. Compared to nonmutants, rogue brace roots are gangly grotesqueries plucked from a Tim Burton nightmare. Also, rogue brace roots differ in color from their nonrogue counterparts. I.e. Purple roots = mutant; Yellow roots = nonmutant. Sometimes these colors are reversed though, so stay flexible. Moving one's gaze up from the shovel's target, rogue stalks typically grow taller than nonmutant stalks. Sometimes as much as two or three feet! Still, rogues can be shorter too. Again, stay flexible. As for gender, both male & female corn plants "go rogue," but males tend to do so at a higher rate. Male rogues also tend to make themselves more visible than the females, so you'll want to scrub the buffer zones (picture frame) thoroughly. Finally, rogue leaves hue a darker green. Plus, they're wavier. Kind of like succulents. And that's it. Keep your shovel sharp, your head up & your eyes down. Find rogue—Kill rogue.

So easy a dog can do it:

Although the bullmastiff was MO-ed to guard livestock (apprehend poachers), Bob & Mona Sturgis's dog Zena preferred Rogueing. I rarely saw her happier. There'd be 10 – 12 of us rogueing four blocks each per pass behind her. And Zena would shake the mutants, double hard, with her hulking posterior to indicate their presence. She'd even mollycoddle weaker roguers by staying in their lanes, double-checking their work, and alerting Bob—her captain—if necessary.

Zena was one hell of a sagacious dog. And I loved her fanatically. But she proves my point: Rogueing is easy. (At least I think she does. Could be there's a scent to rogues that dogs can detect?)

Two final notes about Rogueing. First, for obvious reasons, keep your shovel down in a thunderstorm! Second, only the Rogueing crew gets to go to Walmart for a group picture day. (As the whole detasseling crew would be too crowded.) We always brought corn plants with us and made funny faces at the camera. But don't worry about those traditions, just go get the pictures made. You'll be glad you did...

Here's one of mine:

(People you'll know from the book... Front row, left to right: Heath, Wendy, Barnes & Dallas. Next row up & far right, Where's Waldo-looking guy atop Dallas's hat: Benjy. Far left, Frankenstein's monster lookalike: Me. To my right, Animal from the Muppets: Aaron Wilkinson's younger brother, Graham. Top row, mustachioed Beastie Boy with cellphone: our beloved crew boss, Bob Sturgis.)

Commencement

Congratulations Reader! You may now adjust the (corn?) tassel atop your cap—You've graduated! I take great pride in your accomplishment. And you should too.

Indeed, when you work hard you should to play hard. It's a Corn tradition. In that spirit, you may recall certain syllabi for "Drunken" activities introduced previously. Well, those lists detail but two of the iconoclastic partying ideas generated inside the maelstrom of an end-of-the-season Corn party.

Now, it's imperative to forge your own Corn experiences. I can't overstress that point. Nevertheless, I don't foresee a problem with giving you a for-instance here.

To that end:

Freshly-diploma-ed Reader, I cordially invite you to attend my 2002 end-of-the-season Corn Bash. Come along me and witness the fine line between playing hard & tempting fate... staring down the gullet of a whirlwind.

Keeper's Mitts

Or *A Righteous Man Falls Thrice*

Today hankers for celebratin'. Been an up-and-down season. Rained like Genesis. Wind gusted in from Revelations. Couple of cornfields spired seven & a half feet tall. One of our short fields was so infested with aphids that the tassels stuck to our hands like caramel apples. But on the plus side—the serious plus side—we haven't run out of pot this year.

But shuck it all in the ear anyway! I've got my Jeep's windows rolled down. Allman Brothers 'Blue Sky' *sweet-lullabying*. The Iowa sun's shining like a smile while I speed east along Interstate 30, ferrying five kegs of dank ass beer. Only problem I've got in this bright sunshiney world is not knowing where in the hell I'm going. My crew boss, Tom Pater, moved our end-of-the-season crew party—usually held at Scranton Camp—out to some park near Lohrville (pronounced Lorryville). He said we needed extra space, as we've been picking up strays all week (detasselers from Missouri Valley, Whiting & Blair crews finished with their own seasons & looking to hang out). Most of 'em brought their dogs, too.

Fortunately, I spot Roman (a.k.a. "Ramen" like the noodles) Holiday, my hometown friend and former roommate, driving his maroon, compact Toyota pickup up I-25. He'll know how to find that park. So I flip him off through my sunroof, to indicate that he should lead the way.

§

Lounging beneath a 20x20 blue-tarp canopy, three Budweisers into the afternoon, acamp at the summit of the roll-

113

ingest of Iowa hills, Bartleby ("Bart") Jessup's mood is sunny. On top of the world. For he spies Alan Hickey, his hometown friend (Conway, AR—same as Holiday & me) and former roommate, striding cagily up the Iowa-style mountainside with Gandolf the Grey's smoking head swinging from his hand like liturgical incense. Hickey's Beagle/Lab pup Anabanana pads along diligently behind him—yipping at the pungent white ribbons.

Hickey shushing, the two arrive at Bart's campsite and duck into its lavish mosquito-netted atrium. Anabanana plops down happily beneath the fug and scoops a dugout.

"It's weed, mushrooms and a little opium," Hickey offers Gandolf the Grey to Bart. "Me, Nicki (his wife) and Jacqueline (Holiday's girlfriend) already started it. So don't light it, or you'll waste it."

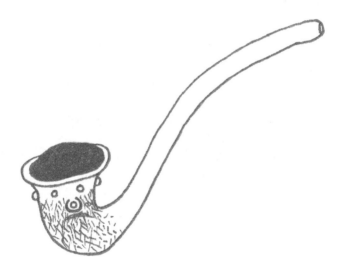

"I've never smoked mushrooms before." Bart accepts the glass piece reverently, cradling its millefiori sherlock stem. He briefly admires its flecky, white & silver artisanship. Then he laps the spittle from his lips & dips a flame inside its cleaved-wizard's-hat bowl.

"What did I just say," Hickey chafes.

"Oh yeahhhhh...," Bart exhales. "Huh? What was that?"

"I said don't light it. You'll waste it," Hickey frowns.

"Oh. Cool cool." Bart nods.

Hickey walks over to the two tents pitched on the far side of the atrium and peeks inside their meshed sunroofs. (A breezy perk of tarp-canopies: no rainflies.) "Where's Ramen at?" he asks.

"Huh?" Bart's ears are full of smoke.

"Where's Ramen at?" Hickey repeats. "Jacqueline said he'd be up here."

"Oh. He went to Casey's for cigarettes. Should be back soon."

"Hmm." Hickey sits down in the vacant camping chair next to Bart. "Well, hopefully not *too* soon," he laughs. (Hickey's laugh is notorious out here in Corn, by the way. It's like those dorky *Revenge of the Nerds* guys, but with a southern accent & a touch of *The Muppets's* Swedish Chef. It's hilarious.)

Bart passes Gandolf back over to Hickey.

In the master's hands, the wizard's skull combusts into clippers, galleys & galleons. These ships roll down the promontory, like a marine slipway, and set sail above the emerald Bluegrass sea below.

"Dude, your dog's butthole's'n eyeball!" Bart dynamites.

Hickey nearly blows the drugs out of Gandolf's hat. "What!?"

"There's an eyeball poking out of your dog's butthole, my dude," Bart explains. "And it's staring at me."

"I'm... Sor-ry?" Hickey replies, asea.

Bart sloshes two cans of Budweiser out of his beer cooler and hands one to Hickey. "Don't be sorry. Probably just her third eye."

"What?"

"Or mine. I'm just making a note of it—not (making) a thing (of it)."

"Right," Hickey assuages. "My dog's butthole is an eyeball."

"*Has* an eyeball," Bart clarifies.

"*Has* an eyeball."

"Correct. And it's staring at me."

"Right." Hickey leans back and launches more smoke boats off the pier.

Unconcerned, Anabanana paws excitedly at a root.

Not more than a minute later, Holiday comes careening up the hillside, torpedoing Hickey's foggy armada. He arcs wide round the campsite, speeding, then tailwhips his truck to a stop behind the tents—half the drugs still fresh in Gandolf's skull.

"That dude's got a nose for drugs," Hickey sighs.

§

"Now?" Bart bounces impatiently.

"Not yet," Holiday instructs, downshifting into second gear & puffing the Basic Light 100 stuck to his lips. A cigarette brand he's dubbed "Stepdads" this season—to great fanfare & adulation.

Begrudgingly, Bart takes his hand off the console's emergency brake. "I'm telling you man. It was an eyeball. And it was staring—"

"—NOW!" Holliday interjects.

Bart's hand teleports back to the console—where he clicks the release button & yanks the brake up before his arm can visibly rematerialize.

Holiday cuts a hard left, till the wheel's grinding up against the steering lock, swinging his Dachshund-sized pickup into a fishtail. Smooth as air travel. Then he gooses the engine and spins the wheel back to the right, quick as a ship helm.

I mean, what choice do they have? This park hasn't been

mowed for weeks. Grass is lusher than the soccer fields back home. Plus, it's slick from all the rain.

It's like a racetrack of grease out here!

"Woohoo!" Holiday fist-pumps.

"Whoopee!" Bart yeah-babies.

§

Cal "Flash" Gordon grew up in Conway. But he was three years behind all of us. Same as the rest of his Ultimate Frisbee friends.

It's a real generational rift.

Hickey walks over to the Lohrville Park's manse-style pavilion—to better watch Flash give chase to a spinning blue disk. Flash whizzing past tents—red, green, blue, yellow, orange—has brought to Hickey's mind, suggestively, a hummingbird too hopped up on feeder-fed sugar water to stop and smell the flowers. Flash's skills are electric. There's no denying that. But perhaps they're gained through performance enhancing drugs? Hickey believes he should investigate.

Hungry for sandal straps, Anabanana doggedly follows her Papa.

Closing the gap betwixt blue frisbee and blue frisbee desire both rapidly & in slow motion, Flash's fleet feet blur like Sonic the Hedgehog's. His scraggly-ass, rookie detasseler beard? Left to dangle in the air several yards behind those cartoon wheel-o-feet.

It's official: Flash's speed is unnatural. Of course, Hickey first started noticing this phenomenon five days ago—when Flash pulled one more block of corn than he did.

Hickey finds a picnic table to sit upon. From whence to hawkeye for further confirmation.

Anabanana dislikes this new elevated site of her Papa's sandals very much. Happily, the familiar scent of Mom approaching soon melts her umbrage.

"I figured it out," Hickey apprises his wife. "Flash's got some amphetamines. Or, at the very least, some new shit from GNC."

Nicki laughs. Ironically, hers sounds like chirruping songbirds. She kind of looks like Snow White too... but really tan. "Hey there sweetheart," she greets Anabanana. Then she takes a seat on the picnic table's bench, beneath her husband's perch, to better scratch puppy belly.

The family Hickey looks on.

As a whizzing, blue UFO crosses into the imagined boundaries of an orange-cone endzone, Flash launches himself. Like a rocket. Laser-guided and focused. Nose cone pining. Just aJet-streaming awind the currents of immortality. All for a goddam frisbee. Admittedly, a well-thrown frisbee: now mere inches off the ground—hewing dandelion puffballs.

At that very same moment, from atop his perch Hickey can see Holiday's tiny truck crest the concealed mesa behind the endzone. Knowing his is a view unshared by most, Hickey, laboriously, stifles a massive heehaw.

From her lower vantage, Nicki spies Holiday & Bart seconds later. In contrast to Alan, the revelation makes her jaw drop... and the tan depart from her face.

Flash meanwhile continues to soar. Blissfully. Missile-locked & confident.

His teammates, unaware of the performance-enhancing drug rumors (and too loyal to entertain such accusations anyway), rip-roar for their champion. Bursting with pride.

Even the opposing team's all ahoot & aholler. Celebrating what passes for a highlight play in this game.

And, there's a growing audience of fans too. Completely uninterested mere moments ago, a dozen detasselers & their very good dogs look on. Cheering wildly.

Flash grasps effortlessly for his prize. It's a sure touchdown...

"HONK!!! H-H-H-HONK! HONK! HONK!" blares

Holiday's truck, stealthily racing into everyone's view. He & Bart buzz the endzone like they're *Top Gun*'s Maverick & Goose. Prompting Flash to catch the long-journeyed frisbee, after it skips off the ground, square on the nose: An incomplete pass.

Quick as they came, Holiday & Bart speed off. Cackling like coyotes.

Hickey starts heehawing uncontrollably, thrashing around atop the picnic table like a boated fish. Anabanana watches her Papa's savory, spinning sandal straps. Rapt.

Meanwhile, Nicki, the other Ultimate Frisbee players, the spectators & their dogs, collectively exhale a loud sigh of relief.

§

Temporarily sated on donuts and mudslides down by the creek, Holiday & Bart streak back up the hill and skid to a stop acenter the pavilion's central breezeway. Then they alight, snickering, and bob on over to my beer garden—a horseshoed array of picnic tables with kegs on top.

"How's the Killian's looking?" Holiday asks, lighting a cigarette.

"It's going fast now," I answer. "So I figured I'd go ahead and get the Shiner Bock flowing."

"Good thinking," he says.

"Fill 'er up?" Bart hands me an empty Gatorade bottle.

"Wish y'all wouldn't have pissed off Flash and them," I say, pouring. "They're slurping the Killian's down now out of spite."

"Nah dude," Holiday counters. "That's just how the first keg always goes."

"Maybe. Still, I already had everything set up down at the soccer field. But then I had to move it all up here—to keep the peace."

"It's way better up here anyway," Holiday says. "On top of the hill. Under the pavilion. In between the two fields."

"But what about the keg stands?"

"We're not playing wiffle ball dude. People'd be throwing up."

"Definitely," Bart endorses. "Plus, we might break the taps off with the soccer ball."

"No." I hand him his beer. "We wouldn't." Then, with a shit-eating grin I pull a milk crate out from under one of the picnic tables. As both Holiday & Bart know, I've been eyeing several stacks of these outside of the Carroll grocery store all season long. What they don't know, but will recognize immediately, is that I stole some while the clerks fetched our kegs. Seemed like a fairly low-risk caper. Especially considering the crates sat next to the loading dock—where they told me to wait. I stole a whole stack, then threw some trash bags over them.

Once the aha moment saturates, we all feel like we're thirteen again & back at church youth group. Like there's thirty people praying around us in a circle, and one of us farts.

"BWAHAHAHAHAHAHAHA!!!" We lose our shit.

"There you go," Bart encourages me. "Loosen up man. It's a party."

"Yeah. You're right. Speaking of... Check this out." I open my weed tin and extract a conical, caveman-club doobie of dank ass nuggets.

"Now that's a muther fuckin joint!" Bart shouts.

"Shhhh," Holiday & I scold him.

"Sorry sorry," Bart whispers.

We scan each side of the hill to make sure the horde didn't hear.

Then, I light the dooby. Carefully. Quick to douse any harbinger of an uneven cherry. Once I'm satisfied, I exit my beer garden with it and saunter around to Holiday's truck.

I prop my foot up on the back bumper. Buuut... the metal's all wet & caked with grass.

Sure enough: "Whoooops!" My paddle-foot sandal slips, and I fall—the back of my noggin aimed at a floor of mortared stonework!

My first countermeasure—which I've learned often proves the most consequential in avoiding calamity—is to jump off of my other leg.

And it works: I begin to plummet more buttwards than headwards.

For my second move, I rock my enormous doobie forward—to swing my momentum.

I land hard, but safely, on my ass bone—holding the joint up like a candle.

Its cherry? A perfect round rose.

And I thought we had a good laugh over the milk crates!

Cackling-coyote-mode Holiday & Bart help me up, and I pass the weed. Which reminds us anew to shut the fuck up—lest we accidently summon the horde.

§

My rookie year, the end-of-the-season Drunken Wiffle Ball game was like our Super Bowl. Same thing my second year. Then last year, my third, all of a sudden we're playing Drunken Kickball like it's still the Super Bowl: a difficult transition. After two or three beers though, I managed to cope.

But this year is too much! Two games! Soccer *and* Ultimate Frisbee! NO obligatory keg stands. Hell, it feels weird enough just being at this park (instead of Scranton Camp).

Us soccer hooligans are playing seven-on-seven at the bottom of the big hill, across the creek from where Holiday's truck tore up the grass earlier. Presently, I'm charging the left touchline, playing left defensive back out of position. Holiday torched the other team's keeper for two early goals, so now they've got the shift on—away from my side of the field. And Bart, our squad's best playmaker, keeps feeding me the ball over here. My upfield crosses have been keeping the pressure on, but now my sweaty feet keep sliding around in my sandals.

Blistering, I lengthen my stride. Holiday, Bart & company await my cross.

Got to get there first though. My counterpart—right defensive back on the opposing team—is Alan Hickey. He's been camping in the box—helping their keeper—ever since Holiday's second score. But now he seems intent on defending this ball. Which really sucks for me, because Hickey's fast as a comet.

Better lengthen my stride some more—It's kinda my go-to move. All out of speed—especially with these sweaty feet; I'm at breakneck already.

Goddam Hickey's fast! "Fuck you Hickey!" I intimidate. Uselessly—he just broke the sound barrier. If I don't cross this ball in stride, I'm sunk.

Left foot, right foot—My stride's nine feet if it's an inch.

Left foot, right foot—Maybe even ten.

Left foot, right foot—

—"Whooaaaaaarrrrggg!" My Chocos prove no match for Hickey's Tevas.

So now I'm flying. Soaring through the air like some goddam Ultimate Frisbee player. Ground's whooshing beneath me... but the grass keeps getting further away? Feels a bit unnatural. Much like my perception of Time. How long have I been up here?

Behind me, everybody looks worried. Hickey in particular.

Quick to quell their fears, I grin & wave like a doofus. Like Mr. Bean. Instantly, Holiday & Bart's fear faces vanish. But, the gag backfires with everyone else: They look even more concerned than before.

As I begin my descent, I notice the soccer ball caroming out of bounds. Anabanana's chasing after it. She's so cute. Peanut brown fur with a white-striped forehead. Bart's been telling people he saw an eyeball in her butthole earlier. But I think he was just hallucinating off of that posh mélange of drugs he smoked with Hickey & Holiday. Muther Fuckers.

Oh shit. Here comes the ground!

"OOF!" I belly flop.

"HOLY SHIT DUDE!" Hickey arrives first. "Are you alright?"

"Oh yeah," I say coolly, brushing myself off. Hickey hands me my broken sandal and I toss it toward Anabanana. "No worries. You?"

Relieved, Hickey belts out his signature laugh... It takes a while. "Thanks for not taking me with you," he finally says. "That could've gone a lot worse."

"No problem," I say sitting up. "I'm pretty good at falling down."

"HEEHAW!"

Rapidly, we're surrounded by rejoicing teammates.

To whom I propose a beer break.

Unanimously, it's agreed.

(Here comes a formation chart for our middle-of-Iowa, *Field-of-Dreams*-style, All-Arkansas All-Star Soccer Game. Don't skip the notes that follow it or you'll miss important character introductions.)

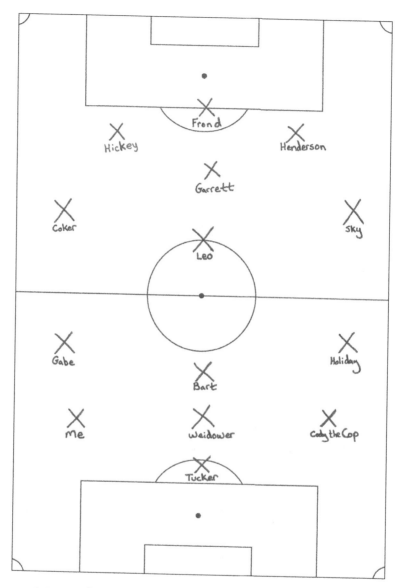

My squad:

Right forward, Holiday. Attacking midfielder, Bart. Left forward, Gabe Greene—a third year detasseler from Newton County. Right defensive back, Cody the Cop—another third year, Newton County kid; we started calling him "Cody the

124

Cop" his first year, quasi-affectionately, and it stuck. Defensive center midfielder, John Paul Weidower—rookie detasseler, son of Little Rock doctors so he played on all the best club teams growing up. Left defensive back, Me. Keeper, Tucker Pruett—a rookie Newton County kid; Like Gabe & Cody the Cop, Tucker's one of our crew boss Tom Pater's role-modeling projects from their hometown.

Opposing squad:

Right defensive back, Alan Hickey. Left defensive back, Gil Henderson—part of Flash's crew of Conway rookies; immune to the charms of Ultimate Frisbee. Keeper, Frond Greene—rookie detasseler from Hendrix College. Center midfielder, Garrett French—Frond's roommate at Hendrix; both freshmen. Wings, Coker and Sky—two Eureka Springs hippies from the Whiting crew; neither one knows a damn thing about soccer, but their virtuoso hacky-sacking skills translate nicely. Lastly, to balance out the teams, our buddy Leo Case from Conway, who we finally convinced to detassel this year (same as Bart), is at striker. Conway has produced a handful of semi-professional-caliber forwards in recent memory. Leo's the best of the bunch.

§

Holiday hangs a toothy grin out his driver's side window. Riding shotgun, Bart maestros to an invisible orchestra. Even quiet Jacqueline, squished in between the two, seems rosily uninhibited. It's a happy truckful that rolls to a stop inside the park pavilion, abreast to my beer garden—where Hickey, Nicky & a dozen more carousers are congregated, quite pickled.

"What's up, dickheads," I greet the new arrivals. "This ain't no drive-thru."

"Dude! We're whipping tailslides and donuts down in that field again," Bart delights. "You should hop in!"

"Yeah man. We're rounding up more people," Holiday adds.

"Sounds like a bad idea," Nicki pooh-poohs, playing another round of tug-JJ's-broken-sandal with Anabanana.

"Well, I've been watching them joyride all day," I say to her. "And I think it looks like fun."

She glowers.

"Sweet," Bart nods. He turns to the group, "How 'bout the rest of y'all?"

From across the picnic tables, rookies Garret, Frond & Alex (Frond's girlfriend) all blurt out, "We're in!"

"Hell yeah!" Bart salutes.

"Tucker? Gabe? Y'all want to come?" Holiday asks from inside his truck—leaning over Jacqueline.

(Over these past four summers, nary a Conway hooligan has ever invited one of our crew boss Tom's Newton County kids to do anything. Not once. So should Tucker & Gabe be leery? YES! But they're both drunk as shit.) "We're in," they slobber.

Next, Holiday leans all the way out the passenger's side window, smothering Jacqueline. "What do you say Weidower?" he cajoles his longtime soccer rival.

"Oh... What the hell," Weidower assents.

Bart attaboys Weidower, then he grabs three beers from me.

I ask Hickey if he'll watch the kegs while we're gone, knowing Nicki won't let him join us, and he starts working the taps before I'm done asking.

"Watch out for this back bumper folks," I announce, hopping in first. "It's slick as shit!" This time around, I step up on the back tire. Then I trundle over the bed wall and into the truck's grooved, polyurethane bed liner. With my full beer unsloshed, I scooch up against the cab.

Then I open the little window and peer inside:

Holiday's hunting for the perfect soundtrack, as usual.

Jacqueline requests Red Hot Chili Peppers.

Bart, Wu Tang.

I'm about to say Blind Melon, when two beefy legs shoot over top of me. All hairy & brazen.

It's just Weidower though. He's doing a Superman/belly-flop pose atop the roof.

Next I watch Frond, Garrett & Alex rattle the tailgate. Hard. Testing its durability. Satisfied, they climb aboard back there: Garrett & Frond at the corners, Alex in the middle.

Tucker & Gabe hoist themselves up next—taking a seat on the bed rail (passenger's side).

Somehow I miss Henderson's arrival. But now he's sitting on the rail (driver's side) yelling "Hurry up!"

Over at the beer garden, Flash nods in response. Looks like he'd probably be over here already, but Hickey's dickishly slow-pouring his beer. Finally, he wrestles his cup away and heads our way.

Stridently, Flash walks up to Holiday's driver's side door.

The tension mounts... thick as the Guinness in our cups.

"What's up fuckhead," he says.

Holiday smirks. "Well... hop in muther fucker!"

Prior to the Touchdown-foiling episode, Flash's perception of Holiday fell somewhere between idolization & hero worship. (No different than how Holiday, Hickey & I felt about the old guard when we were on the come up.) But of course, that was before the bloody nose.

"Cool," Flash says nobly.

And with that, the tension disappears! Good vibes reign supreme.

Flash jumps aboard next to Henderson,

& we're off...

"E-brake! E-brake," Alex yells, her long green & brown hair

127

rippling like the overgrown, patchy grass in our wake.

"Yeah! E-brake! E-brake!" Frond hoots.

"E-brake E-Brake E-Brake!" Garrett cheers.

I look around the truck bed at the rest of the faces. All aboard emphatically want Holiday to pull that E-brake.

Then I look inside the cabin. Holiday's smile's grown wider than the gap in his front teeth. And yet, neither he nor Jacqueline nor Bart have a hand on the E-Brake. Holiday whips the steering wheel to the left, then jerks it back to the right. Flinging our rear end into a mud shower.

When we straighten back out, we're aimed at a long bald patch. And Holiday's eyeballing it like a halfpipe.

"E-brake E-brake E-brake!" resumes the Chorus.

(Reader. If, like many of us in the truck bed, the timing of these appeals for "E-brake E-brake E-brake" confounds your ability to analyze upcoming events, please rest assured: there will be NO PULLING OF THE E-BRAKE. Full stop. Both of Holiday's hands are on the steering wheel—I can see them quite clearly. Also, Jacqueline's hands lay folded atop Holiday's CD case, and Bart's waving his arms around like a conductor again. Thus, I do solemnly swear for the record: we *will* be sliding into the approaching bald patch the ordinary, regular way—sans E-brake. I mean, if you really think about it, the math works itself out readily. Holiday & Bart were alone or with Jacqueline for all their previous jaunts. But now, we've added 1,500 pounds of human mass onto a 3,000-pound truck. E-brake? Erroneous.)

Soon as Holiday cuts the wheel hard over that bald patch, our front passenger side tire starts digging in. Like a tiller. It's reticent at first, for a second or two. But then the muther fucker's drilling for oil! That bald patch churns into a divot, a ditch, and then a ravine! Front tire's pulling & juddering so hard, it's steering Holiday.

Then the back wheel catches. And it starts digging in too; even though this goddam truck's front-wheel drive. (Maybe pulling the E-brake would've helped us out?)

128

Aaaaaaand we're two-wheeling!

(Somebody once told me that drunk drivers often survive fatal car accidents—while their victims do not—*because* they are drunk. Being inebriated makes you go limp, apparently, wildly increasing your chances. Now, I don't actually know if that's true. But it's the only thing I've got to go on right now.)

"Stay loose! Stay loose!" I advise Holiday, Jacqueline & Bart through that little window.

"Are you fucking serious right now?" they ask me entirely with their eyes, through the rearview mirror.

To which I ocularly reply, "Yes. Why the hell do you think I'd bother saying it, given our present circumstances, if I wasn't serious? You three better stay loose or I'll crawl through this fucking little wind—" But they shift their attention away before I can finish.

So I move my ministry. "Stay loose," I preach to the terrified faces horseshoed around the bed rails. "Stay loose!"

Being as how there's only one way to lead people—in front of them—I settle my chin to my breast & let my arms dangle, assuming the posture of a floppy scarecrow.

Tucker & Gabe disembark first. And that's when I know we're fucked. Sure, things didn't look good before. What with the two-wheeling and tilling. But it wasn't until now, watching Tucker & Gabe slip off the rail, that Doom flushed over me. A moment ago, our Fate, quite literally, teetered. But now the momentum has turned. Decisively. This is a car wreck. And we all know it.

Well, all of us except for maybe Tucker & Gabe. Those lucky bastards just fell against the levee we've been digging up in our wake.

They bounce off it, unharmed, like a couple of squirrels.

That creek over there'll never flood this park again. Our levee's five feet high and rising!

Above me, looks like Weidower's done playing Superman. He's got those tree-trunk legs of his pulled up into a crouch.

Truck's slanted 45 degrees now. But Weidower manages to spring upright anyway. Like he's Kelly fucking Slater!

He rides the wave atop the roof just long enough to secure his balance.

And leaps...

Then he hits the ground arms first.

Back at the tailgate, Frond, Alex & Garret hold each other's hands in a chain. Three terrified eighteen-year-old Hendrix College kids (a.k.a. "Brats") just went from the pinnacle of fun to staring death in the face. Yet all three exude a preoccupation with the safety of the other two. Nonverbally, they plead to one other: "Survive me."

Pretty damn life-affirming, that.

And then poof! Now you see 'em... now you don't. Frond, Alex & Garret tumble backwards, linked...

to safety!

Meanwhile, Henderson, Flash & me in the truck bed, and Holiday, Jacqueline & Bart in the cabin continue our two-wheeled journey. Atilt. Onward down.

Now's the time. Follow my lead, Henderson gestures to Flash. Then he squares his footing on the bed wall and jumps...

The Muther Fucker lands on his feet! With relative ease even.

But,

without Flash by his side.

Our rear axle groans. Bout time, really: We've been bulldozing this retainer wall through the whole second verse of Radiohead's 'Airbag.' Anyways, it shakes the hell out of us. And foils Flash's attempt to bail: his sneaker toe gets caught in one of the bed liner grooves.

We're tipping over. Flash quickly regains his footing, then scrabbles up & over the side of the truck—which could be described as the top of the truck, at present.

"Stay Loose," I shout. "Stay Loose!"

"BOOM!" The axle bursts, pulsing through our bodies like a shockwave.

A gale gusts over me.

Whirring.

Whirling.

Whipping my floppy scarecrow body left to right, right to left, left to right.

It's a roiling ocean of Wind...

"OOMPH!" I hit the ground.

A tire spins above my ear. Buzzing like a box fan. Smelling like burnt plastic.

Lohrville Park's lush, rain-soaked sod has caught me like a glove! Or rather, like a sponge. A spongey glove? Ah, I've got it: like keeper's mitts. I'm lying here pinned betwixt mangled machinery and mound of mercy quite comfortably. Eyes mushroomed, nose burning, ears ringing, but otherwise snug as a bug in a rug. Somehow got my forearms raised up to protect me. (Thank you floppy scarecrow!)

Even better, Holiday, Jacqueline & Bart look uncrushed inside the cabin.

Wouldn't know it watching the rest of our crew yelling & screaming & stampeding down the big hill though. It's like watching a battle scene from *Braveheart*. Imagine William Wal-

131

lace, played by Alan Hickey's Gargamel-looking ass, leading his army of warrior-poets down from the highlands to fuck up an English garrison. Such is the spectacle I'm witnessing. Detasselers charging into danger. War dogs barking alongside.

Quite a heartening sight for a guy in my position.

Then, for some reason the weight of this goddam truck surges, dramatically.

"Ooof!"

(Turns out, as we wrecked over our levee, Flash slid off the side of the truck. Which, as we've discussed, was actually the top of the truck, cardinally, at that moment. Anyways, somehow the physics of all our whirly-birding got him stuck underneath the rear passenger's side tire. Kind of like me (with the rear *driver's side* tire), except Flash's knees got pinned up to his chest & he didn't have a truck bed between him and the tire.

"Fuck this," he decided. Sagely. And with an adrenaline-fueled leg squat, Flash pushed that tire and its accompanying car guts up and off his person. Adding its weight to the mangled pile of Toyota sitting atop of yours truly. Flash had no way of knowing that though.)

"NOOOOOO!" Holiday's mortifying plea pierces us all to our Souls. "STOP," he cries. "YOU'RE GONNA CRUSH MY HEAD!"

I look up at Hickey & his Braveheart army and give them my best It's-okay-I-just-had-the-full-weight-of-this-thing-on-top-of-me-anyways face. Suggestive-like.

They release the heap and let it settle back down.

Which works! Holiday stops screaming! "All right! I'm good I'm good," he shouts.

Hickey sprints around the truck and opens the driver's side door, skyward.

Sitreps are discussed. I can hear the conversation through that little window—Holiday & Jacqueline are both uninjured, but Bart's unconscious. As he's got a history of concussions from soccer, that's a worrying concern.

"Your head okay," I ask Holiday thru the window.

"Yeah... Man, I thought you were dead."

"How's Bart?"

"Not good."

"Best to get him out of there?"

"Yeah... Probably so."

"Jacqueline, you good in there?" I catch her gaze in the rear-view.

Solely with her eyes, she responds, "Most assuredly not."

"Can you hold Bart's head still?"

"I believe so. Though I'm debilitatingly frightened," she eyeballs.

Then I address the army. They're all kneeling around the heap again, securing handholds. "All right. My left ankle is caught under something. So this might break my foot. Coker? Sky? Will you two get behind me?"

"Sure."

"Sure."

"Great. Now, if this thing crushes my foot, y'all be ready to drag me out."

"We got you dude!"

"Okay," I nod to Hickey. "Let's do this."

"You sure?" he generals.

"LIFT IT UP!"

Guess whatever jigsaw puzzle of spilling-out car innards that saved Flash stuck around for my foot. 'Cause when Hickey & the army heave, the truck rolls up onto and over something else! A tire or a rod or something, probably. Fuck if I give a shit—It sets me free! I squirt out from under there like that soccer ball me & Hickey double kicked earlier. Damn near knock Coker & Sky over. Barreling—much as one can crab-walking—right past everybody. My butt hardly more than a foot off the ground.

And I don't stop scooting for a looooong time.
Till that wreck looks far away.
Till it feels yonder.
Then, I take a deep breath and hug the grass.
When suddenly, I'm bombarded in puppy kisses! Ana-
banana slurps her wet tongue up and down my face—as if my
cheeks were sandal straps.

Much like Flash, Henderson, Tucker, Gabe, Alex, Frond &
Garret, I return to Holiday's mostly-upside-down truck. Where
we genuflect against the frame, ready to lift—Hickey & the
army having ceded the job. Weidower wants to help, but his
arm's sore and swelling. (He has a slight fracture to his left ulna
that his doctor parents will soon diagnose).
   Inside the cab, Bart's regained consciousness, but he's woozy.
Jacqueline holds his head to her breast.
   Holiday gives us the okay, and we hoist.
   When the undercarriage hits the ground, it shakes the
whole fucking truck. Violently. Then it bounces, settling.
Groaning like an old porch swing. Makes us all even more wor-
ried about Bart.

§

   "Only 'cause you had a truck on top of you," Nicki says.
"I'll forgive you." She's just finished chastising me for using my
cigarette lighter on this posh mélange of drugs.
   She & Jacqueline are playing nurse to Bart right now. We
got him out of the truck just fine. But he got his bell rung pretty
good. So we don't plan on letting him fall asleep anytime soon.
   Still, the mood's quite jubilant up here at the pavilion. I pass
Gandolf the Grey over to Flash, then I head over to my beer

garden. Anabanana tags along: anxious to resume our game of tug-JJ's-sandal. (She already chewed up that broken one, so now we're working on the other.)

Ain't a person around me who doesn't understand how lucky we got earlier. Notwithstanding, the wreck did sober everybody up. So now I'm not sure if what's left in these kegs is gonna last us through the night. Oh well...

I got whiskey.

(In the years to come, the preceding Corn Story will become renown as "The Miracle Truck Wreck." But that title's a little too on the nose, isn't it Reader? So I changed it.)

Afterword

Welp, that's all folks! Hope you've enjoyed the ride. More importantly, I hope I've answered "What the hell is corn detasseling?" to your satisfaction.

Such has been my goal: to reveal the true nature of Corn. To manifest its character. NOT to objectively record events from twenty years ago. These are true stories, yes. But I sure didn't match all the facts to the page. For there's no surer roadblock to Truth than fastidious objectivity. Every former lawyer knows that. Plus, Memory is the most notorious of liars anyway.

If nothing's ever perfect, how can you *eliminate* errors? Corn's answer to this paradox is 99.7%. "You pull me 99.7% of my tassels," Corn says, "and you'll be perfect enough for me." And doesn't that just kinda feel right? Equitable? I know it works for me. Otherwise, I'd never be finished with anything. Cause you've got to get out there & live while you can. That's for sure. Now more than ever. Yadda yadda yadda...

You know, the older I get, the less sure of everything I become. Wisdom's hard work. And I wasn't really on the job till a few years ago. Lucky for me, Aaron Wilkinson already expressed the point I think I'm trying to leave you with here. So, why don't we just give him the last word? He sure steered us right a few chapters ago.

Coincidently, I've always called the following "Aaron's Yoda Verse."

Just a Man (third verse) – Aaron Robert Wilkinson

Now look at me, I'm just a man living in this world.
And I have no idea what any of our lives are for.
But one thing that I've noticed from my first tiny breath
is that we all breathe the same, and our last one ends in death.

So live your lives as you decide and don't be surprised
if all your dreams come true when you simply do instead of try.
When what's laid before you is nothing like you'd thought it'd be...
Is when you take comfort in the thought
*   that your life is all you've got.*
So gain and lose and pay your dues,
*   and what you choose will be your destiny.*

Acknowledgments

Thanks to Wendy Blackwood, Jewels Dabdub, AB Dickson, Avery Honea, Jake Honea, Kirk Jordan, Liz Larson, Gabrielle Lawrence, C.F. Lindsey, my Mom, Ed Robson, Will Shelton, Mark Spitzer, Matt Stroman, David Sutherland, Stephanie Vanderslice, Jack West & Graham Wilkinson for helping to shape the kernels of this Cornpendium.

Thanks, in advance, to The Strokes for not suing me for reproducing their *Room on Fire* album dedication.

But most of all, Thank *You*, Dear Reader. I'd still no doubt be navel-gazing in free verse had you not mused this book. Thanks for hounding me. What the hell is corn detasseling? indeed. Now you know: It's Corn! Come to think of it, you got any more suggestions? I fear we may have caught lighting in a bottle here.

Made in the USA
Columbia, SC
08 August 2023

21213033R00078